McGraw-Hill
INDUSTRIAL ORGANIZATION AND MANAGEMENT SERIES
L. C. MORROW, *Consulting Editor*

HOW TO CONTROL
PRODUCTION COSTS

McGRAW-HILL
INDUSTRIAL ORGANIZATION AND MANAGEMENT SERIES
L. C. MORROW, *Consulting Editor*

BETHEL, ATWATER, SMITH, AND STACKMAN—*Industrial Organization and Management*

BETHEL, ATWATER, SMITH, AND STACKMAN—*Essentials of Industrial Management*

CARROLL—*How to Chart Timestudy Data*

CARROLL—*How to Control Production Costs*

FEIGENBAUM—*Quality Control: Principles, Practice, and Administration*

FINLEY, SARTAIN, AND TATE—*Human Behavior in Industry*

GARDNER—*Profit Management and Control*

GRANT—*Statistical Quality Control*

HANNAFORD—*Conference Leadership in Business and Industry*

HEIDE—*Industrial Process Control by Statistical Methods*

HYDE—*Fundamentals of Successful Manufacturing*

IMMER—*Layout Planning Techniques*

JURAN—*Quality-control Handbook*

KALSEM—*Practical Supervision*

KIMBALL AND KIMBALL—*Principles of Industrial Organization*

LANDY—*Production Planning and Control*

LAWSHE—*Principles of Personnel Testing*

MAYNARD, STEGEMERTEN, AND SCHWAB—*Methods-Time Measurement*

MICHAEL—*Wage and Salary Fundamentals and Procedures*

NEUSCHEL—*Streamlining Business Procedures*

SMYTH AND MURPHY—*Job Evaluation and Employee Rating*

STANIAR—*Plant Engineering Handbook*

TOOTLE—*Employees Are People*

YOUNG—*Personnel Manual for Executives*

HOW TO CONTROL PRODUCTION COSTS

PHIL CARROLL

Professional Engineer
Author
"Timestudy for Cost Control"
"Timestudy Fundamentals for Foremen"
"How to Chart Timestudy Data"

FOREWORD BY

BRUCE WALLACE

Financial Vice-President
Otis Elevator Company

McGRAW-HILL BOOK COMPANY, INC.

NEW YORK   TORONTO   LONDON

1953

HOW TO CONTROL PRODUCTION COSTS

v

FOREWORD

The whole subject of "How to Control Production Costs" that has been covered so thoroughly by Phil Carroll in this book has always been important and has become increasingly so during the past two decades.

In the early days of the industrial era of this country, there were relatively few competitive manufacturing firms. Through reinvestment of earnings, these firms increased the output per man hour, lowered their prices, increased their volume, and enjoyed the prosperity that invited competition. As the number of competitive firms increased, the necessity for the control of production costs increased. The firms that were successful in the control of their production costs survived. Those that did not appreciate the importance of the problem, or failed to find a satisfactory solution to it, became business casualties.

It is doubtful that there ever has been a period in the industrial history of our country when the necessity for controlling production costs has been as great as it is today, or when it has been as difficult to accomplish.

One of the factors which makes the problem urgent and difficult at this time is the fact that industry, in general, has enjoyed a period of at least twelve years of unusual prosperity. During that time, there has been less necessity for careful control of production costs than usual because, during the World War II period, emphasis was on getting out production. Cost was a secondary consideration. In the postwar period, because of the pent-up demand for civilian goods that had not been available during the war, emphasis was again on production, regardless of price, rather than on the control of production cost.

For industry, in general, it has been a period of large volume, high prices, and general prosperity, which combine to breed carelessness in the control of production costs. Many of industry's younger executives have gained most of their experience in this lush period. That makes it difficult for them to appreciate fully the necessity for close control of production costs in normal times.

There is much evidence indicating that this comfortable situation is beginning to change. While defense work still sustains the general level of production, there has been a change from a seller's to a buyer's market in many lines. Resistance to price increases is apparent, although costs continue to rise. Some day our economy will drift or dive into a corrective period, when there will be lower volume, lower prices, and higher costs. At that time, the firms that have learned to control production costs will again be the survivors, as they always have been during similar periods in the past.

The convenient practice in some complex industries of applying overhead expenses uniformly to all products, resulting in similar costs for a mixed group of products, will not be sufficiently accurate in a highly competitive market. The success of many firms will depend upon their knowledge of the accurate costs of individual products.

This book could well be divided into two parts of almost equal value: (1) the first chapter, which deals with the necessity for the control of production costs, and (2) the other 25 chapters, which describe in workable detail the means of accomplishing the control with diversified products.

To the top executive, the most important part of Phil Carroll's book is the first chapter, in which he develops the necessity for controlling the cost of production in order to offset the deterioration in the standard of living in this country resulting from inflation and high taxes. He will get from it inspiration for constantly supporting his junior executives in their work of carrying out the difficult steps involved in the establishment and maintenance of the control of production costs.

> BRUCE WALLACE
> *Financial Vice President*
> *Otis Elevator Company*

New York, N.Y.
September 29, 1952

PREFACE

My first book, "Timestudy for Cost Control," emphasizes the need for sound work standards. My concern goes beyond those of fair and equitable work measurement for incentive purposes. That is vital, to be sure. Without successful incentives, I find that work standards have little practical use because pressures are applied to adjust them to something different. Therefore, my belief is that we should have both standards and incentives. Combined, these can serve as the foundation for the more important cost-control structure. After all, if industry fails to make profit, we have no further use for either timestudy or incentives.

You might say that this book is an extension of my first. In it, I have tried to show ways to use the foundation we call a common denominator. Such is necessary to bring our diversified products together. And in most plants, our best common denominator is standard time. We should use it to get more facts in costing. Better costing is required to guide industrial management. Our costs are up and rising. Our competition is growing from those abroad we have equipped and trained. Our tax load gets heavier and more burdensome. We have no escape but to make more profits. Industry pays all the bills.

To meet our obligations in our American way, we must try to turn out better products at lower prices. This means cost reduction through methods improvement. In this effort, good timestudy can be most helpful. But here I'm stressing also other tools of management—particularly engineering, production control, suggestion plans, and quality control. None of these contributes, however, that does not pay its way. Hence, the basic necessity for controlling costs.

You can't find out what costs are by the "Dead Hand of John Gough" methods as G. Charter Harrison calls them. Much of the costing that I've observed does not apply our complex overhead expenses where they belong. That is the subject I endeavor to unravel in this book. I hope my efforts will prove helpful to those willing to break away from management by imitation.

Many of the ideas expressed here have been stolen from others. Many examples have been taken from my own experiences. Identities have been concealed in most instances on purpose. Yet, I must mention C. D. "Chief" Dyer, who put me in the position where I had to learn, and Bruce Wallace and De Voitsberger who taught me what I did absorb. Also I am indebted to some folks who should be mentioned specifically. J. Carlisle MacDonald granted me permission to use illustrations from the 1950 Annual Report of U.S. Steel. Edmund Ruffin said I could use the chart showing "First Six Years of Model T" taken from General Motors' excellent publication, "American Battle for Abundance." Miss Bettina Bien opened the door to quotations from the Foundation for Economic Education, Inc. H. T. "Tom" Hallowell, Jr., sent me the originals for the cartoons illustrating the paths of special and standard products through our overhead paper mills. L. C. "Jack" Morrow took time from his crowded schedule to make my first chapter readable.

Beyond these are four to whom I am indebted. Charlie Thomas got after me to "write it down." My son, Phil, who was working in the accounting field, read the material and made constructive suggestions. My secretaries, Mrs. Shirley Mangin and my daughter-in-law, Lee, struggled through the endless details of preparing the manuscript. I hope you appreciate their help as much as I do. Your comments and criticisms will be most welcome.

PHIL CARROLL

Maplewood, N.J.
October, 1952

CONTENTS

CHAPTER 23

Measure indirect operations for incentives, and correct allocation of costs to products

CHAPTER 24

Other tools like suggestion plans and quality control are useful in cost reduction

CHAPTER 25

Get out the results for the period like newspaper reporting to cut down the extent of cost leaks

CHAPTER 26

Systems do not control costs. People must take action to correct causes that reports point out

CHAPTER 1

WHY WE NEED COST CONTROL

Mr. Webster says, "Control is to exercise a directing influence over." You could interpret his definition to mean holding a static condition. But that would be dangerous. We must offset

PER CENT INCOME OF SALES

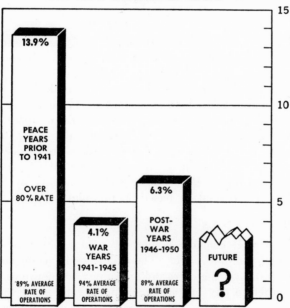

Fig. 1. Chart showing the "Profit Squeeze" in our important basic industry, steel (U.S. Steel).

rising costs. We have to make progress. We dare not lose our competitive positions. So I want to insist that reducing costs is part of controlling. What we lose in one part of cost, we must more than save in another to assure profits.

Raising prices is not the answer. That course does not im-

1

prove our standards of living. We attained our high level by turning out better products at lower prices. The "raises" in our living standards were created by the better management of machines, materials, and men—and, I like to add, *time.*

Higher productivity is the underlying cause of our nation's progress. In this advance, managements have been guided by controls supplied largely by cost accounting. They have been aided by industrial engineering. But we have to devise still better direction finders because profits are being siphoned off.

Repeated wage increases, price controls, and punitive taxes have cut profit percentages (Fig. 1). Break-even points are treacherously high. To survive under the "ability to pay" formula, we have to make more profit.

WHY MORE PROFIT?

Profit is the incentive in industry. Profit is the security of jobs. Profit is the "seed corn" of progress and expansion. Profit is the taxpayer.

You may say, "We're doin' all right. We make a nice profit." Lots of firms do. Yours may even show the typical "huge profits" the bureaucrats attack and the unions scream about. Those "huge profits" are both unusual and unreal. They flowed in without any real competition. Those dollars are debased. Part of the "profit" came from the markup of inventory produced at earlier dollar values. Part was created artificially by the over-absorption of depreciation based on preinflation costs.

PIGS AND POTATOES

Price and wage controls cannot solve the problem of spending more money than we have. These devices have no connection whatever with printing extra dollars to pay for potatoes we don't want in order to pay out still more money to paint them blue. On this merry-go-round, "The people pay thrice, in prices today, in taxes tomorrow, and in the loss of their savings the day after." [1]

As a result, the lathe hand "needs" more money. When he gets it, his food bill goes up because prices go up. So do his taxes, because he is paid in dollars instead of steak and potatoes. He thinks he has part of his problem solved with raises tied to

---

[1] Pettengill, Samuel B., Inflation Concerns Everyone, *The Reader's Digest,* October, 1951.

the Bureau of Labor Statistics cost of living. He thinks he will get closer to a solution by legislating his taxes into the Bureau of Labor Statistics cost-of-living index. The index as now compiled is a "snare and a delusion" because income taxes are "a major factor in the cost of living of almost every union family." [2] All these remedies are pointing to the paradox that exists in Great Britain where "economic planning by the government has provided free dentures for the populace but almost no meat for them to chew."

SOME RESULTS

If you want to see some results, study the startling figures given by Lowell W. Herron.[3] Here's how values have declined.

Year	Value of Bond, in Dollars with Interest Added	Merchandise These Dollars Would Buy at 1940 Prices
1940	$ 75	$75.00
1941	76	70.89
1942	77	65.75
1943	79	63.83
1944	81	64.55
1945	83	65.15
1946	86	63.46
1947	90	58.50
1948	94	57.43
1949	98	60.66
1950	100	57.00

Neither can we live on borrowed money indefinitely. Look at how much of our future is mortgaged already.

Federal Debt [4]	*Per Family*
1929	$ 571
1939	1,165
1950	6,786

[2] Living-Cost Index Assailed by Union, *New York Herald Tribune,* Sept. 16, 1951.

[3] Herron, Lowell W., *The Clarkson Letter,* February–March, 1951.

[4] High, Stanley, In Washington It's Waste as Usual, *The Reader's Digest,* July, 1951.

WHY AFFORD TAXES?

We don't solve the problem, as someone suggested, by "setting" 25 per cent as a top limit on taxes. That approach is like taking aspirin for a headache when what we need is castor oil. How can you progress in costs or attitudes or incentives by saying "that's all you can have"? And no reference was made in that limit setting to shifting the tax load. No offer was made to correct progressive taxation so that industrial leaders would have more incentive to develop our industrial "gold mines."

WHAT SECURITY?

Now, I am not opposed to security. I would like to have some myself. It would give me considerable peace of mind if I had a pension to count on. But taking money out of the left pocket to put it into the right is vicious.

My question is, "Do these protective devices undermine incentives? Do we work as diligently when our futures are taken care of?" Those who founded our country left behind what security they had to come here where they had none at all. They had to rely on their own abilities. It was this self-reliance, this individual initiative, that made us excel.

Perhaps I have confused cause with effect. Maybe we made such great strides because business leaders could keep some of the money they earned. We know they did have more incentive to take risks, to work hard, or to build the better mousetrap.

OUR GOLD MINES

We seem to be going downhill at a rapid rate. It looks to me as if we are in a helluva mess. As I said to one union business agent, "You may get a huge kick out of tossing a five-dollar bill on the bar for a snifter of whisky. But it won't taste a bit better than when you paid a quarter for it." The best solution I can see for us is to go to work. We have to get back on the track of straight thinking and work for greater productivity.

I don't pretend to be an economist. As a matter of fact, they didn't teach economics to engineers in 1918. Yet I like to think my second-grade arithmetic is all right. The answer I come up with is, "Industry pays all the bills." Industry creates the only real wealth we have—production. And industrial management has within itself the only practical solution to our problems. Many factors are involved, of course.

To correct our conditions we must first admit that we cannot get something for nothing. Here, that means we cannot get special securities for ourselves "for free." "Everything produced is *produced by the people,* and everything that government *gives the people* it must first *take from the people.*" [5] Such schemes cannot work any better than increasing wages without increasing prices—if we agree that "sharing the wealth" destroys initiative. I would include here the selfish view of "getting mine while the gettin's good."

Also I think industrial managements have to make enough profits to pay the bills. And these bills we pay must be large enough to allow for expansion to provide jobs for our growing population. We have to get out of bankruptcy one time or another.

THE PROFIT MOTIVE

Profit-making companies are the life-giving fountains of youth in our country. To make profits, our companies must have customers who will pay more than costs and be satisfied with their purchases. "Millions of consumers, making their choices, create demand for the goods most wanted. Factories making these goods expand and prosper. Goods not wanted because of high price, poor quality, bad design, etc., go unsold, and companies making them either improve their price and product or go out of business. It is the consumer, not the government, who determines what shall be made, in what quantity, at what price in relation to cost; and competition forces producers to reduce cost." [6]

ALL YOUR COMPETITORS

Don't be misled by the term "competitor." He is not only the fellow who makes your type of products. He is two other guys also. For one, he is the fabricator of products that can be substituted for yours. More dangerously, he is everybody that

[5] American Federation of Labor, *Labor's Monthly Survey,* p. 3, July, 1949.

[6] "Lower Costs through Human Engineering," pp. 10–11, The American Economic Foundation.

makes any product your customers want and will buy instead of yours with the money they have available to spend.

All who produce are in competition for your customers' dollars. The degree of competition is determined largely by the distinction your customers make between necessities and luxuries. Some will buy an automobile and go without decent food. Notice how many television antennas stick up from shanties and tenement houses. Others will put all their spare cash into gin mills. You and I may put our extra dollars into homes or life insurance. But the average man wants the basic necessities, namely, food, shelter, and clothing, first. His wife, who spends the money, always has a list of wants longer than your arm. She chooses from her list those things that seem to give the greatest values for the dollars left after she has purchased the "necessities" for her family. Thus, a great part of industry competes for the remaining consumer dollars.

It is true that inflated money increases purchasing power, if we think in dollars. But we see all around us that our extra dollars do not buy what the theorists said they would. How can they, when costs go up also? The thinking has to be in real wages—not dollar wages.

CUSTOMERS COME FIRST

Our customers start the ball rolling. Customers employ all of us to make things they are willing and able to buy. Their free choice can cause our business to shrink, to coast along, or to expand. And notice, John Q. Public does not ask "Who made this hat?" when he goes into the store to buy a new one. He doesn't ask if the company that made it earned a profit or what its costs were. If he plans to pay $5 for his new hat, he is interested only in the quality offered for his money. And I'll bet he would be very resentful if you asked him what his "ability to pay" was before quoting the price.

"The real and ultimate boss of industry is the consumer," says James F. Lincoln. "If we are to please him, he must continuously be given lower prices for a better product. Only so can industry expect to continue to sell him increasing quantities." [7]

[7] Lincoln, James F., "Incentive Management," p. 10, Lincoln Electric Company, Cleveland, Ohio, 1951.

EGG OR CHICKEN

In simple terms then, the customer puts us in or out of business. He furnishes us what we call income or sales. The amount of income depends upon price, to a large degree. But price cutting is not what I'm talking about. That kind of reduction comes out of profit. I've already tried to show that we need more profit —not less. At the same time, I admit that there is room for more of the "five and dime" principle of "small margin, large turnover."

Right here, you might say, "Phil, you're inconsistent. Is it industry or the customer that pays all the bills?" I think it's industry. My reasoning is like this. We started with huge natural resources that were here from the Creation. Only when the pioneer made a *surplus* of shoes, candles, or cloth did we have any swapping. Our resources became refrigerators and automobiles only through even greater *surpluses* invested in tools and machines. Customers buy more only with *surplus*. Industry maintains itself and expands only with *surplus*. Obviously, if the customer did not buy, there would be no production and no wages. Then, we would be back in the Stone Age again. You figure it out, if you can. It's beyond my capacity to say whether the egg or the chicken comes first.

COST REDUCTION

We can agree that more *surplus* must be in the customer's hands before he can buy more of the things his wife wants for the family. Printing-press purchasing power won't do it. You can see that easily enough if you imagine a sudden overprinting of two dollars for every dollar of currency. War production and Works Administration projects can't provide the surplus because they are overhead or nonproductive.

If you believe as I do, then we must create the increased purchasing power by lowering relative prices. I say relative because dimensions change each time we stretch out our thinning dollar. What I'm leading up to is that our progress toward greater volumes and profits must come from lowered costs that permit relatively reduced selling prices.

"The only thing that makes anything not sell is a too high price," [8] according to Henry Ford. And when he was being criticized by the court for making "frightful profits," he said the company was "organized to do as much good as we can for everybody." [9] He plunged into mass production. He set out to make a car for the "multitudes." "The original price of the car had

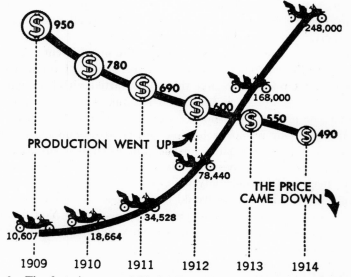

Fig. 2. The first six years of Model T. (*Charles Franklin Kettering and Allen Orth, "American Battle for Abundance," published by General Motors, 1947.*)

been $900. Now Ford had pared it down to $360 and up to midsummer of 1916 the company had made and sold 1,272,000 cars." [10] "It sold for as high as $900 and as low as $265." [11]

What Henry Ford accomplished is most strikingly shown in Fig. 2, The First Six Years of ·Model T.[12] This chart shows

[8] Richards, William C., "Last Billionaire: Henry Ford," p. 54, Charles Scribner's Sons, New York, 1948.

[9] *Ibid.*, p. 54.

[10] *Ibid.*, p. 58.

[11] *Ibid.*, p. 397.

[12] Kettering, C. F., and Allen Orth, "American Battle for Abundance," p. 68, General Motors, 1947.

clearly how customers multiply with each decline in price. The reason is obvious. As your prices come down, you can place your products within the reach of ever-expanding markets. Besides, you may remember, Ford more than doubled wages in 1914 when he raised the plant minimum from $2.34 to $5.00 per day.

HIGHER PRODUCTIVITY

You can say, "But the automobile is different." And it is. S. Stokes Tomlin says, "Automobile manufacturers have progressed so far that if they were still using methods they used in the early 1900's, the average car today would cost $60,000." [13] Nevertheless, the basic cause of this revolution in our way of life was Ford's resolve to make a car for the "multitudes." His one model and his conveyer belt were resulting methods. These and many other method improvements he used did raise productivity. Costs came tumbling down. Prices were slashed repeatedly.

Someone said, "We should work more diligently to increase the size of the pie instead of quarreling so much about the size of the piece." Our way to enlarge the pie is to increase productivity. This we can do in several ways. The one we think of first is the use of better methods. That way takes more capital—profits—savings—more and better tools. The money comes from cost reduction.

Improvements are necessary whether you seek higher productivity or lower costs. Don Copell puts it this way. "Remember that no war, no strike, no depression can so completely and irrevocably destroy an established business as new and better methods in the hands of an enlightened competitor." [13a] Remember also that engineers are working nights, Sundays, and holidays to make obsolete your products, your equipment, and your methods. These men are in the design departments of your competitors, your suppliers, and your equipment builders. Consulting engineers are helping them get ahead of you. Gerald Wollam

[13] Tomlin, S. Stokes, Productivity Standards—Warehousing, *Advanced Management,* p. 19, March, 1951.

[13a] Copell, Don F., "Work Simplification Training," American Manage-ment Association Production Series 157, 1945.

says, "Don't try to compete today using yesterday's method if you expect to be in business tomorrow." [14]

One way to increase productivity and to lower cost is by eliminating work. We can cut down the extra work made necessary by faulty workmanship, poor equipment, incomplete engineering, and lack of planning. Thus, we can easily get more output by changing nonproductive effort into productive work.

Then, of course, we work for reductions of lost time—waiting. And, right here, I want to make certain that we are thinking alike. We must study our indirect as well as our direct operations. Is not overhead work including "distribution" even more susceptible to method analysis and improvement than the direct? The answer is "Yes." It is true if for no other reason than that we have given most of our attention to "direct labor."

BETTER INCENTIVES

And, do we not need incentives to keep people actively interested in the success and progress of our companies? Here I'm suggesting incentive as a philosophy, an attitude of mind. It is an excellent way to spell the simple term "work." Willingness to work is the attitude we need to resurrect. In this effort, incentives can be of real assistance. They can have a vital effect if we can make them both the means of reward and the attitude of accomplishment.

BETTER MANAGEMENT

Incentive philosophy or attitude is what James F. Lincoln calls "incentive management." He pounds on the note that we, as individuals, have far more abilities than we ever put to work. He says, "The first step for the industrialist to take in his program of development is to recognize the fact of the limitless possibilities of man. . . . The leader, therefore, must produce the opportunity and apply the incentive to his people so that they call on themselves to the necessary limit to develop that particular quality or ability [needed] at that time of crisis." [15] What he means by crisis is explained earlier when he emphasizes the

[14] Wollam, Gerald, Notes for Summary, NNJ SAM, 3d Annual Conference on Cost Reduction and Cost Control, Oct. 28, 1949.

[15] Lincoln, James F., "Incentive Management," p. 56, Lincoln Electric Company, Cleveland, Ohio, 1951.

fact that world leaders would not have developed as such had they not been forced to by the "white heat of crisis."

Some of what he is talking about is seen in the "executive development" programs cropping up here and there. These seem very important to me. As Allen Ottman puts it, "Another aspect of competition . . . is the ability of the management of a company to compete with other managements in the industry." [16]

COST-CONTROL GUIDES

We develop men for the same practical reasons that we develop new products and new methods—to make profits. But what do we know about the profits from executive and supervisory development? Very little. Sure, many companies measure salespeople against a percentage of sales-dollar income. But what does that mean, with profit and material in the yardstick? Actually, a sales department could appear to be doing a pretty good job while selling everything below cost. Other companies have budgets or overhead ratios to control expenses. Usually, budgets are certain amounts less than the departments have been in the habit of spending. Overhead ratios are even looser and are wholly unreliable.

Beyond these, and excluding direct labor, we have almost no measures of executive performances to go by. We have few costs that are correct. Yes, I know that labor and material are figured to the fourth decimal place. But overhead is spread on with a shovel. So our product costs are bound to be wrong except on the average.

Then, how can we tell whether or not a "developed executive" is doing a good job? How can these men who are "coming along" judge for themselves what they are accomplishing? I think we have to get some realistic cost-control yardsticks to guide them. We must separate fact from fiction. We must report results while they are news. And we must use "payment by result" incentives to draw out the best in those men we are relying on to build our industrial future.

[16] Ottman, A. H., Standard Pricing Base to Promote Corrective Action in Product Pricing Policies, *NACA Bulletin,* October, 1949.

CHAPTER 2

SEPARATE FACT FROM FICTION

When the Wright brothers flew their first plane at Kitty Hawk in 1903, the chances are they had no other "instrument" than a gasoline gauge. They didn't need any better controls. They could see where they were at any time in flight. Charles Lindbergh had more dials in his Spirit of St. Louis when he crossed the Atlantic in 1927. Today, the number of instruments, dials, and gauges deemed necessary to navigate an airplane is enormous. You've seen the panel boards in front, on the sides, and overhead that the pilot uses to steer the proper course safely.

In the same period of time, it seems to me that operating a business has become every bit as complex. And while probably I'm stretching the point, I say that our business steering instruments have lagged way behind the requirements. Maybe the instruments would have developed if the managerial demand for them had been sufficient. I might add that the demand should come from management. As I put it, "A manager has to have enough knowledge of accounting to know what to ask for." Management must have the right information to take the actions, do the directing. Accounting is only a service function—scorekeeping as it were.

COST ACCURACY

Skilled accountants will tell you that accurate costs are not obtainable. No amount of money you might be willing to spend can provide accurate costs. Therefore, our concern is only with degree of accuracy. Are the costs off by 10 per cent or 100 per cent?

In general, more accuracy costs more money. In the shop, we think of tolerances of plus or minus .002 inch as costing us more than plus or minus .010 inch. But often, we can get closer tolerances at the same or lower cost by changing methods. We may grind the close fit at less cost than turning.

12

As a matter of fact, however, accurate costs are meaningless to progressive managements. Accurate costs would have to be static. For dynamic managers, slide-rule figures are close enough. For dynamic managers, costs serve only as momentary gauge readings. They propose to change the costs, whatever they are. That is their function. They are interested in trends—downward, as a rule.

Trends cannot be found in the cost reports of many plants. Great numbers still figure "actual costs." Actual job costs are not worth the paper they are written on. Another way I have phrased this is, "An order number is issued so as to have a label for the wastebasket used to collect cost sheets. When the basket is full, we add up the total and call that the job cost." This reminds me of a story I saw in *The Reader's Digest*. R. M. White tells of "a salesman inquiring, 'Don't you people find it hard to obtain the necessities of life up here in this rugged Ozark country?' The native replied, 'We shore do, pardner, and half of it ain't fitten to drink after we get it.'" [1]

You won't agree, I know. And I hasten to admit that any costs are better than complete ignorance of what is going on. But the point is, actual costs can be so misleading. The trouble is not with the costs as such. It is with the philosophy behind them. The urge to get in "everything that belongs to the job" is what wrecks their usefulness. Three big variables are usually dumped in willy-nilly. These are

1. Setup costs without regard to quantity.
2. Scrap and pieces that disappear.
3. Inefficiencies, rework, and wage-rate variations.

In the small plant and the job shop where lots may be small, these variables cause the costs to jump around like jack rabbits. To make bad matters worse, overheads are applied to the "actual" labor. These fluctuations may be further compounded by using overhead rates that vary with volume changes. With such costs, you don't have anything you can tie onto for control purposes. Constructive actions you may take to reduce costs are easily thrown off by as simple a change as quantity run. You are forced to act on hunch or intuition—common sense we call it. But that

[1] White, R. M., Life in These United States, *The Reader's Digest*, p. 43, September, 1943.

isn't reliable enough for running a business. As Stuart Chase puts it, "Common sense tells us, among other things, that the world is flat and that it is impossible for men to fly." [2]

You cannot take correct action quickly when you have to rely on long-term averages to smooth out the variables. Consequently, you suffer the losses in the cost bulges that occur between corrective actions.

Actual costs are only one step above the old-fashioned "what's left in the till" method. They reflect the accountant's fetish for balance. He must account for every penny. His attitude is correct. It's the application that is all wet.

It's like what happened in a New York plant. Someone had sold them a punched-card system. They had one card of holes for each bit of work. There were several cards for each man-day. Everything was put in readiness for sorting to job costs. The trouble was that cards were mislaid. Too many men were short in pay every week. I was asked to help unscramble the problem.

This is an example of losing our perspective. We forget that the plant won't shut down even if we don't figure costs at all. But it won't run very long either if men don't get paid. That is one reason why I have always tried to keep all of a man's time together on one sheet of paper.

EASY SORTING

Knowing that, several men I know have designed whole sheets with many perforated sections. Their purpose was to give me what I wanted, and then to tear apart the sections for job-cost sorting. Perhaps, I should have been pleased. Instead I said, "We will do nothing to make it easier to continue job costs. Our plan is to get rid of them." My reason was and is that you cannot tell where you stand from costs that contain so many variables.

Summing up this point, I think one basic fault we must overcome is the confusion between accounting and control. Of course, your accountant must account for all the money. He must balance his books. But that does not mean that he must charge every penny to those jobs processed within the period. The dif-

[2] Chase, Stuart, Social Science: Friend of Management, *Personnel,* p. 256, January, 1951.

ferences can be shown separately. And if you are to get any place in cost reduction, you must use the exception principle. You must show variations from some fixed reference base. You must have some standards to go by. *O¢s*

[handwritten margin note: Important]

DESPERATION CUTS

The usual actions taken to control actual costs are what I call "desperation cuts." They are sudden, arbitrary slashes made to restore conformity. J. P. McClintock calls this "crisis engineering." "In short, it is the technique of perpetually pumping water out of the bilge without repairing the hull." [3]

The desperation method of cost reduction is evidence of lack of control. It's like using stock chasers to bolster up a production-control plan that doesn't work. Stock chasing interrupts production. It concentrates on the "short" items at the expense of the whole output. So it is with across-the-board cost cuts ordered in desperation. This is action, yes. It is like running a fire department. It amounts to locking the stable door after the horse has been taken to the butcher shop.

What is worse, the good operations are penalized. The poorly run departments may have all the help they really need after you make such cuts. And if the desperation method becomes the one everybody expects, perhaps those departments that were good will protect themselves for the next cut with plenty of cushion. Besides, the figures may show that you attained your goal when, in reality, those gains are lying around in piles of unfinished work.

Yes, trimming costs will reduce losses. You may even restore a margin of profit. Just the same, such actions are working on effects. They do not get at causes. That's like cutting down weeds in your garden. They will grow again. You know that you will have to repeat the cutting if you do not dig out the roots. You can rave and rant about costs being too high. Are the excesses due to inefficiency or to extra work? Your department heads can argue that they need more help. Do they? Has work been added, or has performance fallen off? You can't tell without measures and specifications.

[handwritten margin note: Work on effects rather than the causes is bad]

[3] McClintock, J. P., Seven Control Techniques for Effective Management, *Proceedings,* Industrial Management Institute, p. 50, May, 1950.

PLANNED ACTION

Control, as we want to discuss it, is the sound, planned, stabilized type. Control is the steady day-by-day maintenance of performance standards. To get control, you must have facts to go by. You must work from causes.

Causes are of two kinds in our analysis. One type includes all the work considered necessary to the proper functioning of the organization. Such work becomes the standards mentioned earlier. The other causes are those behind the variations from standard.

If costs are too high, we have to ask ourselves two why questions:

1. Why do we have excesses over standards?
2. Why do we have such costly standards?

If costs are too low, we have the same two questions in different forms:

1. Why are we able to operate below standard costs?
2. Why can't we hold to less costly standards?

In oversimplified form, planned cost control is like quality control. You have a standard, with a broad or narrow band of allowable variations. Actuals that fall outside the tolerance limits are "out of control." Your method or process is out of adjustment. And the signal calls for an investigation of cause. If the variance shows a persisting trend toward better performances, you lower the control limits.

You can place control limits of 15 per cent defective about an actual. That is like taking past performances as your standards. Or you can say, "Fifteen per cent is too much. We have to get down to 3 per cent." By either approach, you have set standards. That is the most important step in control.

But there is a big difference in cost between 15 and 3 per cent defects. A loss of 12 per cent defects may put you out of business. That is vital. You do not need cost control when your company has folded. So I want to liken the difference to cost reduction. We might call it dynamic cost control.

GETTING FACTS

To cut from 15 to 3 per cent defects, you would have to analyze causes. You would find several. Each would have its own range of variation. Some would have large, others small effects on the total.

It is clear, however, that you cannot get any place by working on the total. You cannot reduce the defects, except perhaps temporarily, by issuing orders to cut 12 per cent. The defects reported may drop. You may find those not reported under the benches when you take inventory.

You must find out what several causes are in a total. Then you can see those that have the biggest influences. You know then also what the total will be if you can cut one or more of the big causes. This is the same approach you use to set standards for costs—direct or indirect. You have to build up your totals from the parts.

You can never solve your cost-control problem by cut-and-try operations on a total. Sure, you can whittle off 15 per cent and get a result. But you don't know what elements of the total were changed. Nor do you know what remains in the new total. Worst of all, you don't know that 40 per cent might as easily have come off the expense.

Stating this in the positive, you must define what is to be done. In timestudy, we call it specifying the method. Having determined the work to be done, you can build up the total time for carrying on the function. I say time rather than money because wage rates change frequently. Time measures will hold for longer periods.

COST JUGGLING

To get control, you need better facts. You should strive for the right answers. You should not juggle costs like the men do in the shop to fudge the answers. You should not hoodwink yourself like some folks do. A Pennsylvania company charges most of its advertising "to Clover because it can carry the cost." A Maryland plant always shows the foundry running at a loss. An Ohio plant refuses to apply certain costs to one division because the boss's son would be shown up unfavorably. Several companies take out part of the overhead because "we can't get the business if we charge the full amount." And so it goes.

Tell me, how can you tell where you stand if you juggle costs? How do you know where the profit or loss really is? How can you plan for next month or next year from costs that are fudged? How do you know what products to go to work on or to abandon? How can you appropriate money for plant expansion or sales campaigns on such fallacious costs?

I think it's refusal to face facts. That is so silly. Ordinarily, it doesn't make a penny's difference in the current end result. But it can make a whale of a dent in the future. The reason seems obvious to me. Three factors affect tomorrow:

1. Your business is growing, if for no other reason than the increase in population.

2. Your markets are shifting with style changes, competitive forces, and population drifts.

3. Your products are diversified, and some are sure to be pushed more than others.

So I maintain that you must separate fact from fiction to know where you are heading.

DECENTRALIZED PLANTS

You would expect to get more factual costs if each of your products were made in a plant by itself. That would not necessarily follow because charges could still be juggled. Advertising, just mentioned, and general overhead expenses are typical. Yet, we think we approach the ideal with decentralized plants.

We have a common application of this thinking in department or burden center costing. The idea is a good one. But facts deny this. Like the isolated plant, only the actual costs created there are factual. The remainder is allocated. And there is another more pertinent detail. One department in the usual plant does not complete one product. It works on several. Other departments add work to those same products. Again, we run into cross charges and reallocations. All these factors make the complex problem I indicated at the start of this chapter.

PLANNING PROGRESS

We should not throw in the towel. It isn't that difficult. It requires only a little straight thinking and some resolution. First, we must want to get the facts. This alone will require breaking down some habits. Maybe we have avoided the facts. More likely, they have been hidden in the "reallocated reallocations" of accounting.

Then, we must recognize the necessity for progress and profits. That means cost control and cost reduction. These can come only from knowing where the profits or losses are, and taking actions. Pushing the profitable products will improve the over-all result. Reducing costs will do the same thing, only more so. Curtailing the sales of unprofitable products or reducing their costs will also add to progress.

But people cause costs. Hence, cost control and cost reduction depend upon people. And now we are back to the basic cause of business success or failure. I plan to discuss this subject at some length in Chap. 21.

Here I want to make a point on the relation of factual measures to the performances of people. It is that first we must know what work is to be done. How else can your people know what is required of them? Please don't get me wrong. Maybe your job definitions are already taken care of. Sure, we assign work and we instruct people to do certain jobs. That's like a so-called production schedule made up of "wanted dates." Do you have the capacity and materials to complete those orders? You can't tell. You have neither volume of work nor sequence scheduled. "Wanted" is all you know about it. All this means that we need to know how much work there is in any assignment if we are to measure accomplishment.

Then people will be more satisfied with their work. They will know before you do how their performance compares with expectancy. And you will have to report results factually to be fair to the people and fair to yourself. The results should be reported promptly. Each delay allows the performances to get further off the course. Incentives to hold the course will help greatly. Yet, in the final analysis, we need to develop the skills of all those who make decisions. How can we expect to develop people unless we separate fact from fiction?

CHAPTER 3

FALLACIES IN OVERHEAD COSTS

"Your overhead is too high. We have to cut it down. We can't compete with rates as high as those we've had this period." Have you ever heard such comments? Many times, I'll bet. One reason is because so many managers think in terms of overhead ratios. That's the way they were brought up. They make such remarks from habit. Salter calls it "conditioned reflex."[1] At any rate, the premise is "all wet."

NO FIXED RATIO

In the first place, there is no fixed ratio. You have a different one for every different volume, if expense is in perfect control.

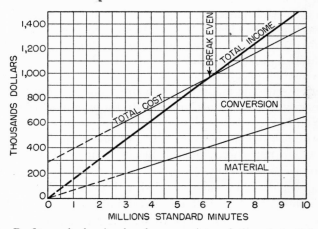

Fig. 3. Profit graph showing break-even point and the substantial cost at zero volume that causes it.

Almost any ratio might show up if expenses were not kept within control limits.

[1] Salter, Andrew, "Conditioned Reflex Therapy," Creative Age Press, Inc., New York, 1949.

Look at the diagram, Fig. 3. You will see that expenses at any volume contain a large constant. The constant is what some call the cost to "keep the doors open." It is largely made up of the fixed portions of everybody's salary. Obviously, too, it includes the relatively smaller "fixed costs" like depreciation and taxes. It is an imaginary figure because volume never reaches zero until after the sheriff has taken over. But it is a very substantial cost

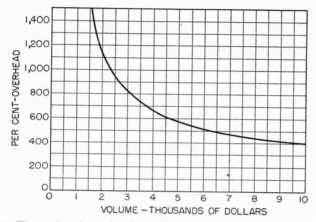

FIG. 4. The ratio of overhead to labor varies greatly according to the volume of business a company does.

in a going concern. It may be as much as 25 per cent of the total cost at normal volume, including material.[2]

Such a large constant cost shifts the overhead ratio automatically with changes in volume. The shift is a result of simple arithmetic. If you divide 50 by 50, you get 1, or 100 per cent. If you divide 50 by 25, you get 2, or 200 per cent. The shifting of the overhead ratio with changing volume is illustrated in Fig. 4. In simple algebra, the effect of the constant on the overhead per cent is that of a reciprocal $(1/X)$. It might be expressed as follows:

$$\frac{\text{Constant cost of the organization}}{\text{Volume in dollars}}$$

[2] Carroll, Phil, *Your Overhead Is Too High—We Have to Cut Down, Manufacturing and Industrial Engineering,* December, 1950.

OVERHEAD RATE IN COSTING

Of course, the "too high" comment grows out of thinking of some fixed ratio. Most people use such percentages for overhead or burden. They need them in estimating and costing. But such fixed numbers are current standard rates for overhead. They are figures used to keep volume variations out of the inventory pricing.

Such standards are necessary, in my opinion. Without them, we would price ourselves out of business in a falling market. In reverse, we would give the plant away with rising volume. More than that, I think we have to use such standards for bench-mark measurements.

My quarrel is with the kind of measurement used, apparently without much analysis. To exaggerate, you do not measure distances in pounds. You do not weigh materials by yards. Why say the overhead ratio is too high when we recognize the variations due to volume in "flexible budgets"?

INCONSISTENT THINKING

There is another reason why thinking in terms of ratios is misleading. It is inconsistent with progress. You make progress, as a rule, only when you raise your overhead ratio. Take a simple case:

Your manufacturing man learns of a more efficient machine. You already have one doing a pretty good job. But the new type will turn out more production. On this premise, the labor cost will come down. Chances are the overhead will go up. That will result from taking out of depreciation the remainder of the cost of the old one and adding in the depreciation on the new one. We most likely would double the depreciation costs. We have to pay out so many more of our inflated dollars to buy the new machine. If the old machine is already written off, we are in a worse fix.

MAKING IMPROVEMENTS

So the arithmetic is stacked against you. Everything you do to improve methods raises your overhead.

1. The better your methods, the higher will be your overhead.
2. The higher your productivity, the higher will be your overhead.

In both statements, overhead can mean overhead dollars or overhead rates. Here are the reasons. Methods improvements cost money. You buy or make gadgets, fixtures, tools, and equipment. If you don't spend a dime for any of these, you still have the expense of the people who think up and install new ideas. Also, you pay for lost production and some spoilage while the new methods get under way. All these add to overhead dollars.

Maybe the overhead goes up faster than it should. This can occur when some of the ideas are too expensive. Mistakes are made in the other direction when the labor cost fails to come down to the estimate. Anything can happen if you do not know what your labor costs actually are before the change or afterward. You're in still more trouble, if you don't get facts about overhead costs.

Overhead dollars go up also when you improve productivity. I say that because you spend more in overhead for production control, engineering, supervision, instruction, timestudy, and methods work.

As for overhead rates, these go up in any event when you reduce the productive-labor denominator. The divisor of the fraction is lower and, consequently, the answer is higher. We will discuss this denominator fully in Chap. 4.

STAFF FUNCTIONS

Why introduce planning or production control? That is overhead, all of it. Why deliberately raise the overhead? Well, you say, "It's good business." And the "good" part is that it will pay for itself.

You figure that production control will reduce delays. Then if the delays are in direct labor, as many are, the labor cost is reduced. The divisor is smaller. Again the overhead rates take another hike. The same applies to timestudy or methods improvement. Both are overhead tools used to reduce labor cost per unit. Both have the double-action effect in raising overhead rates.

What about selling and advertising? Are they overhead? They are, in many statements. Well, should we deliberately increase overhead when it's already too high? I know that question is silly. We have to have salesmen to stay in business.

Their expenses and those of engineering, personnel, accounting, timestudy, production control, and many others are direct additions to overhead. They are tools of progressive management. But we can't eat our cake and have it too. We have to recognize the simple arithmetic of overhead rate computation. Also, we have to see clearly this double-action effect on our answers.

WHY STOP PROGRESS?

It should be obvious that our measure is wrong. We agree that we must continue to make progress. Also true, it seems to me, is that progress is made by using tools and devices that become overhead costs. It follows, then, that overhead rates must climb automatically with progress. And again let me emphasize. Any and all of the advanced management tools that reduce wasted time and effort in production cause doubling increases in overhead rates.

Naturally, there is an offsetting factor. We do expand. We have a natural growth due to increasing population, even if there are no other causes for it. This expansion in volume I left out of consideration to avoid confusion. And I mean confusion. We may actually get a lower overhead rate, if we expand volume more rapidly than we increase overhead. Again, this is a simple arithmetic result of dividing a much larger measure of output into a slightly increased overhead.

Let's take two examples. Suppose, first, that our overhead was $100,000 when output was $50,000 of any measure. Our overhead rate then was

$$\frac{\$100,000}{\$50,000} = 2.0, \text{ or } 200\%$$

Now, if the overhead is increased to $120,000 as the output and sales go up to $75,000, then our rate becomes

$$\frac{\$120,000}{\$75,000} = 1.60, \text{ or } 160\%$$

MIXED EFFECTS

But the ordinary accounting procedure does not point out separately the effects of these two compensating factors. We see only a net figure. If it looks good, we are pleased. If it looks bad, we say, "Overhead is too high."

We should not keep on fooling ourselves with overhead ratios or cents per sales dollar pointers. These mechanisms never were reliable. And they are being made worse daily, with our infla-

FIG. 5. The fallacy of overhead ratio. This man is not going very far, but he's happy to be keeping down his overhead. There are plenty of managers like him. (*Manufacturing and Industrial Engineering.*)

tionary moves in every direction. What we need are cost-control measures that are more factual.

Much of this confusion, and the wrong costs resulting, would disappear if we dropped the overhead per cent idea. It clouds up sound thinking. Why have two figures anyhow? Why not put both labor and overhead in the one cost? Total conversion cost is what we have to watch.

Cost does not rise necessarily when overhead rates go up. Sure, it may. But good management does not usually spend money for improvements that increase overhead costs unless the direct costs will come down more than the overhead goes up. On the other hand, cost does not decline if you try to reduce overhead by charging the foreman's time to the jobs in his shop (Fig. 5). Shifting cost from the left pocket to the right does not reduce the total. It only looks that way.

WRONG FACTORS

What we have been talking about holds true as long as you figure overhead the same way. And there are several ways of figuring. Many are incorrect. The result is that most of the costs I have seen are wrong. The errors are not in the computations. They are in the figures used to make the computations. It's a bit like the mistake I made one time. I was working in a plant where drawing dimensions were given in millimeters. I got the correct result in my calculations but the wrong answer because I was thinking in inches.

We do the same thing sometimes with simpler problems. For example, we correctly multiply 3×5 and get 15. But maybe later, we discover that we should have used 7 instead of 5 and our answer should have been 21. If we figure the area of a triangle as length $\times$ width or the circumference of a circle as πd^2, we will get wrong answers.

Do I make my point? I'm assuming that we can add or multiply. Yet the costs are wrong because the starting figures are in error. We get the right answers in solving the formula, but the formula is wrong.

UNIFORM OVERHEAD RATE

If you use a uniform rate of overhead, you apply a constant proportion of expense per hour, dollar, or unit of labor. A uniform overhead rate results from dividing all the overhead expenses by the total of a denominator for absorption. This is exactly the same condition that is used when an operation setup is prorated on a piece standard. It is correct for the average. But it is wrong for all other conditions.

MACHINE RATES

You cannot reach correct conclusions with figure indicators that are not factual. Here's an example of averaging horses and apples. In one plant, we set a drill press near five automatics so that the mechanic could have stabilized production. The drill press stood idle when he had short runs on the automatics and frequent setups. In reverse, he could turn out production on the drill press when he had long runs on the automatics.

Automatics are expensive. But, as we sometimes forget, the higher cost equipment usually requires less work from the man. Reverse conditions are true of the drill press. But George Miller thought of man-time as the controlling factor. So he added the expenses for the two machines. Then he divided that total expense by the total standard minutes of man output. His burden rate was wrong for both. He found out quickly. His costs went up on all the drill-press operations. They went down for the automatic jobs.

DEPARTMENTAL RATES

Expanding our previous example, you can see that departmental burden rates commonly used are greatly in error. The errors are caused by three basic variables:

1. Differences in costs of the several types of equipment grouped in the department.

2. Differences in utilizations of capacity of the different types of equipment.

3. Errors in allotments of overhead costs not related to the work done in the department.

Considering only the first two, equipment cost and utilization, look at Fig. 6. The figures are actuals. That is just what's wrong. The depreciations and other costs stem from a wide variety of actual conditions. The activities (divisors) are those predicted for normal volume. When you put such happenstances together to figure burden rates, any kind of answers can result.

You would expect a high cost per unit of output when you use expensive equipment. Yet, you can see that such a result is true only when the activities of high- and low-cost equipment are reasonably alike. In our example, the activity per machine averages 43,791 standard minutes. The range in per cent of production of the average is from a low of 2 (899/43,791) to a high of 223 (97,371/43,791). Now, I know it is ridiculous to average drill presses and spray booths, but that is what we actually do when figuring a departmental burden rate. So on that kind of average, each work station costs $335 annually. The range is from 29 per cent of the average for the Acme Screw Machine to 359 per cent of the average for the Bliss Press.

Notice that the weighted average of the unit costs is $7.66 per 1,000 standard minutes. This would be a departmental burden rate or a cost center rate if all the other indirect costs were in-

Department 12				
Type Machine	No.	Annual Expense	Normal Activity, Std Min	Tool Cost per 1,000 Std Min
Sipp Drills................	16	$ 3,707.36	761,265	$ 4.87
Upright Drill..............	2	431.87	14,225	30.36
Radial Drill...............	1	234.69	65,925	3.56
Garvin Tapper............	1	379.98	11,670	32.56
Riveter...................	1	197.76	40,359	4.90
Grinder...................	2	353.66	153,765	2.30
Hand Miller..............	2	316.96	21,650	14.64
Milling Machine...........	2	1,094.62	103,072	10.62
Engine Lathe.............	5	1,234.41	117,451	10.51
W & S Lathe..............	4	1,619.26	333,182	4.86
Acme Screw Machine......	1	97.15	58,171	1.67
3½ Screw Machine........	1	182.00	1,045	174.16
P & J Lathe..............	2	807.98	2,508	322.16
Niagara Press............	1	908.99	8,422	107.93
Y & O Press..............	1	329.11	97,371	3.38
Bliss Press...............	1	1,202.98	899	1,338.14
Oaking Shear..............	1	489.38	76,466	6.40
11½ Higley Saw...........	1	261.99	5,465	47.94
Spray Booth..............	2	1,925.13	185,287	10.39
Total....................	47	$15,775.28	2,058,198	
Average...............	...	335.64	43,791	$ 7.66

Fig. 6. A typical machinery shop department with costs showing a wide range from an average that would be applied if you use a departmental burden rate.

cluded. I recognize the dampening effect of incorrectly adding a flywheel amount that includes accounting, timestudy, engineering, and works manager. But without these to hold down the true variation, the low cost per standard minute is 23 per cent of the average for the department. The high is 17,450 per cent of that same average overhead cost. We won't go into the correctness of these cost amounts at this point.

It seems obvious to me that departmental burden rates can be correct only when all activity in the department is in the production of one product. Even when this condition is met, this method of burden application gives you costs only. You have no way to get control as it affects the whole enterprise. You have no way of unscrambling the "reprorated reprorations" buried in a rise or fall of the overhead cost. More about this in Chap. 12.

JUGGLING OVERHEAD

Funny as it may appear to you, some managers take these departmental burden rates very seriously. I'll give you a couple of incidents to show what I mean. Back in 1919, Harry Sanford tried to show me how he made a "saving" by moving an operation from Dept. T with 275 per cent overhead to Dept. W with 250 per cent overhead.

In 1926, the argument came up again. This time, it was with Bill Jones, boss man of the plant. His convictions were strong. After all, he had installed the cost system earlier, as a consultant. His system was based on machine rates.

You see, I wanted to save most of the cost of a helper. To do so would cause us to lose about 17 per cent production in the regular work day. To maintain the same output, we would have to put some production through another machine. The rate for the second machine was $10 per hour. The one we were operating had a cost of $5 per machine-hour. He maintained that the cost would go up when we ran the 17 per cent lost production on the "more expensive machine."

"Bill," I asked, "if we run the production on the $5 per hour machine, what is our overhead cost?"

He said, "Five dollars per hour."

I asked, "Isn't it $15 per hour?" "Now, if we run the product on the $10 per hour machine, what is our cost?"

He replied, "Ten dollars per hour."

Again I said, "It is $15 per hour. We have to get back the costs of both on the production we have, if we are to make a profit for the period."

Well, we talked back and forth quite a while. Then I made the diagrams shown here (Fig. 7). First, I drew curves to show the

budgets for direct labor, overhead, and total conversion. These
were plotted against *per cent production*. The budgets for 100 per

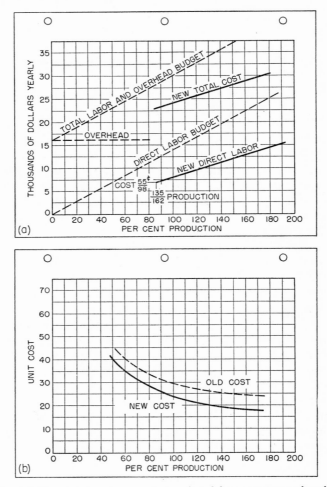

Fig. 7. (*a*) How total cost came down when labor cost was reduced more
than production dropped. (*b*) The relation of old to new costs per unit
of volume.

cent production were $14,000 labor and $16,000 overhead. Then, I
set up a new direct-labor cost line based on the ratio of 55 cents to
98 cents. The operator's rate was 55 cents, the helper's 43 cents.

In those days wage rates were quite a bit lower. And the production was dropped in the ratio of 135 to 162. This new direct labor cost added to the overhead gave me the total conversion cost line (Fig. 7a).

Dividing the budgeted total and the new total by *per cent production* gave the unit costs. You can see how these compare in Fig. 7b. To make a long story short, this convinced Bill. We went ahead on that basis.

SHIFTING OPERATIONS

In A.D. 1951, I bumped into the same fallacy. This time the shift was from one process to another. But the burden rates were in the ratio of 9 to 1. The high burden rate they used came from dividing burden dollars by a low activity figure. The movement of the operation from the low-rated process would lower the activity and thereby raise the burden rate on the remainder. Injecting it into the high-rated department would have the opposite effect.

At the risk of boring you, I want to stress this point further. In another company, we had new buildings and old ones. We had two-story and five-story buildings. Would we change the overhead cost of an operation by moving it from the fifth floor of a new tall building to the first floor of an older two-story building? The burden rates will change if you stick to the actual costs of the buildings. Also you shift the utilizations and thus change the divisors.

Obviously, if an operation is moved from a relatively cheap to a more expensive location, the overhead cost may go up. For instance, the overhead cost of an operation rises when we move a lathe operation to an automatic screw machine. The total cost of that piece should come down if the quantity is large enough to warrant the change-over. Regardless, we must pay for both if we run the automatic while the lathe stands idle.

PIGEONHOLE THINKING

Some methods of figuring overhead give us wrong answers. I'll try to prove this later on. My complaint here is that we let the machine-hour or department-burden rate method pigeonhole our thinking. One author calls it "compartmentalizing." We forget that management, personnel, accounting, and other overhead costs apply to the *work* going through the plant. Such expenses do not go into the department or onto the machine that is not working. Many such expenses apply to people—not to things and places. Yet, the arguments assume that they do because they were allocated that way in computing the burden rate. Factually, these costs do not belong in the machine or departmental overhead rate. They are stuck in there only for convenience in computing job costs. So, if you will leave them out when analyzing a shift in location, you will not be confused. And you will not get erroneous answers like those illustrated here.

You should keep in mind that the products you sell must carry all the burden however distributed. Otherwise, you go broke. You cannot save overhead by rearrangement. You can save it in such instances only under two conditions:

1. When you sell the unused capacity, or, more usually,
2. When you avoid buying capacity for expanded sales.

One story may clinch these two points. I remember tangling with George Smith, President, on this subject in 1925. I tried to show one reason after another why the work I was doing was saving money. Many of my arguments seemed futile. Finally I said, "Well, you must admit that productivity has been doubled in the weave room. Your overhead cost of the product has been reduced."

"Yes," George admitted. "When you started I had a shed full of looms standing idle. Now, I have a shed and a half full of idle looms."

MISLEADING AVERAGES

Next, I want to point out the most common error. This one is the fundamental reason for this book. It is an extension of the averaging error illustrated earlier by the department rate (Fig. 6). The same mistake, often greater in amount, is made by averaging other items of overhead. The one I have found to be misapplied most often is engineering cost. That happens because of my many experiences with tailor-made products. Just to make an illustration, suppose that the engineering cost for motors is $1.00 per standard direct labor hour. For pumps, the engineering cost is $.50 for each standard hour of productive labor.

Now let's work out an example with volume of business changing from June to July. Suppose in June that 70 per cent of our business is in motors and 30 per cent in pumps. In July the percentages are interchanged. The total volume of production remains the same.

Product	Actual Engineering Cost	June		July	
		Std Hr		Std Hr	
Motors	$1.00	70,000 × $1.00 = 70,000		30,000 × $1.00 = 30,000	
Pumps	.50	30,000 × .50 = 15,000		70,000 × .50 = 35,000	
		100,000	85,000	100,000	65,000
Average	...	$ .85		$ .65	

You can see how much the true cost has shifted by noting the averages shown below the two periods. These represent the engineering required. And to use a uniform rate is a mistake.

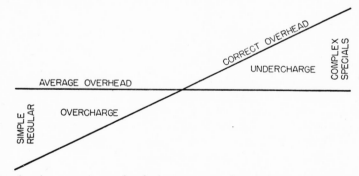

Fig. 8. An average overhead charges more than belongs to the regular products and less than costs to the specials.

Either average would charge more to pumps than the cost. Both averages charge too little to motors.

This is of major importance in all plants that mix special products with their standard lines. The specials are not charged as much engineering as they should be. The standard items are overcharged (Fig. 8). And coming back to our ratios, you don't know whether the engineering payroll should go up or down with changes in volume.

BURIED INDIRECT

I have touched on several kinds of errors to show how we bury our heads in the sand. I think that we take accounting too much for granted. My guess is that many think like John Hayward. He said, "Phil, we *absorb* overhead on our inefficiencies." I countered with, "What you intended to say was that you *apply* your overhead on your inefficiencies."

There is a big difference. We apply overhead. We bury it. We may or may not actually absorb overhead as it is applied. But profits fluctuate without our knowing why. Actually, you can't find out with fallacious thinking and figuring. You have to quit totaling overheads into big piles for ease of distribution. You have to go at this like engineers. Take things apart to see what makes them go. When you look at the parts, the accounts, you can see what's happening. Then you can take the right kinds of action to maintain control.

CHAPTER 4

ERRORS FROM WRONG YARDSTICKS

"Your unabsorbed burden is climbing skyward," your boss says. Then you come back with, "Why don't the sales department get more business?" You two argue back and forth, getting nowhere. Maybe both of you are seeing the trees and forgetting the forest.

Did you ever stop to think that the trouble might all be of your own making? Did you know you can easily rid yourselves of your unabsorbed overhead? All you have to do is make your shop less efficient.

UNDOING PROGRESS

It couldn't happen to you, but repeated pounding on too much unabsorbed overhead produced the result in one plant. The manager hired a lot of people to put two men on one-man jobs. He raised his man-hours, "sho' nuf." The unabsorbed overhead came tumbling down. Of course, product costs hit the ceiling. Inventory was inflated. The manager moved on to other pastures. But the damage was done. It took quite a while to get things back on an even keel.

"Foolish," you say. Yes, I know. Isn't it true, however, that too much pressure can be put on the arithmetic? Reasoned control may tell you to spend in contradiction to the arithmetic.

SIMPLE FRACTIONS

Most people apply overhead as a rate, in costs and estimates. In a department store they call it "markup." And to get an overhead rate in industry, you divide some indirect money by some measure of output.

$$\frac{\$60,000}{\$40,000} = 1.5, \text{ or } 150\%$$

35

Simple division is our method for determining overhead rates. What the money is, we discussed in the previous chapter. The amount may be wrong, as we will analyze more fully in Chaps. 7 and 12. Obviously, if the money is incorrect, your overhead rate will be wrong. The same is true if your divisor is not right. By divisor I mean the *measure of output*.

WHAT IS VOLUME?

In industry, we use many different measures of output. Most folks base their plant overhead rates on labor dollars or man-hours. Some use standard time. Other people prefer machine-hours. These may be actual or standard. A few mix material or tonnage in their divisors. And there are combinations. All these are related to manufacturing. In figuring general overhead rates, we see sales or cost dollar divisors as an added variety. What does represent volume?

If we stick to arithmetic, certainly different measures of volume will give us different burden rates. Any one will give us practically the same cost for the average product. But we don't have average products. We have mixed products. That's why they can't all be right.

And the same questions apply to our overhead dollars. In our simple example, does the $60,000 correspond with our divisor of $40,000? You may say "yes" from habit. Sure, all of the 60,000 are dollars. But not all the same kind. They are not applicable equally to each of the units in the volume divisor. So our overhead costing is in error in two places. These errors are of four general types:

1. We apply overhead to factors that do not measure work.
2. We apply some part of overhead to material costs.
3. We apply overhead to labor that is not salable output.
4. We apply average overhead to products that are not average.

Each of these has a series of variations. I will point out the more glaring. These may be grouped in two types for our discussion. The types are suggested by the following questions you should ask yourself:

1. Does my cost denominator actually measure volume?
2. Is my measure of salable volume correct?

TONNAGE RATES

Tons are incorrect as denominators because they do not measure work done, as a rule. They are inversely proportional to process time. As I express it, "The more work we do on it, the less it weighs." That is the answer I gave Jim Lang when he wanted to simplify our standard setting. He said, "It's too complicated. It takes too long to set a standard. Why can't we use pounds to measure toolroom work like they do at Rotor Grinder?"

My example is unusual. Take the more commonplace. Foundries often gauge their production in pounds and tons. Many price their castings on a pound basis. If they classify their castings by types, they reduce errors somewhat. But the fundamental principle is wrong. Heavy, chunky castings are relatively simple to make. The labor cost per pound is low. The casting cleaning is not very much. The scrap losses are low. Yet, the burden applied is very high in proportion to work done.

At the other extreme is the thin-section, multicored, complex casting. This kind takes lots of molding, coremaking, and cleaning. The loss risks are much greater. But the overhead charged on a pound basis is low in relation to the work done.

Sure, I know that cupola, pouring, and other costs are directly proportional to molten metal at the spout—pounds. However, these costs are the smaller segment of the total. Tying all the overhead to the smaller controlling element creates the same "tail wagging the dog" mistake made in the machine-hour method.

CUBE OR BOX

Let's take an example. You know that a 1-foot cube would be easy to make. Molding would be simple. Coremaking would be zero. Chipping would be very little and scrap losses negligible. The casting would weigh about 440 pounds.

Now let's add a core 11½ by 11½ by 11¾ inches to make this casting a cubical box with ¼ inch wall thickness. Its weight is reduced to about one-tenth. The molding is more difficult, especially if the core is made integral with the mold. Chipping cost goes up. Scrap losses rise considerably.

This example is easy to see. At the same time, is it apparent that the work done varies inversely with the weight? Since it does, we should agree that weight is not only wrong as an over-head carrier, it may not even be related to work done.

Maybe you don't make tons, only buy them. In that case, you may see more clearly what I'm driving at. As a buyer, perhaps you have had experience like Floyd Mitchell. He said to me, "We are having all sorts of trouble with our castings. The ex-cess stock we have to machine off is terrific." Pursuing the dis-cussion I asked, "Do you buy castings at so much per pound?" His reply was, "We do. Everybody does." Then I asked, "Why not buy your castings by the piece? Then, won't the excess stock practically disappear?"

You will admit that it is a waste of good cast iron and valu-able machine time to whittle off excess pounds. The fault lies with the customer. He bought pounds instead of pieces. But you can't blame the foundry very much. It sold pounds. Chances are this was the direct result of the cost system used in the foundry. Similar distortions are made by many cost systems. The chief difference is in degree. Another difference is the form of error.

COST DOLLARS

Dollar divisors that include material can be more incorrect than tonnage. This is the biggest error in using sales dollars for any kind of comparisons. The point is that we are trying to measure work added—not purchased.

To exaggerate, suppose we bought everything we assembled into pumps. Suppose we made everything we put into motors. You can readily see that combining such materials with labor would greatly distort our overhead rate. And this condition I have exaggerated exists in many subtle forms. We use cheap materials in some products. We buy expensive motors and speed changers for other products. You can readily classify these dif-ferences in material content roughly into three groups:

1. Amount of raw material used in small as contrasted with large products.
2. Costs of raw materials used, considering the same amounts of
    a. Expensive alloys or metals versus
    b. Relatively cheap steels and cast iron.

3. Costs of semifinished or finished materials purchased externally rather than manufactured within your plant. Common examples are motors, speed reducers, bearings, relays, valves, meters.

Your plant has mixtures, probably. Also you make some parts today and buy them tomorrow.

For a given mixture, you may think of three degrees of error. The greatest distortion exists where both factory and general overheads are applied to material plus labor costs. The next and quite common condition is where sales and administrative overheads are applied to factory costs that include material. The third condition comes about when we treat purchased items like motors differently from raw materials like sheets, bars, and castings. Materials are only the carriers of your "added value," as some express it. They do not measure your applied skill.

SALES DOLLARS

Besides the errors caused by material content, you have the profit variable in a "sales-dollars" divisor. Also, prices expand and contract. With inflation, they have been expanding since World War II. Yet in mid-1951 we had the big price-cutting contests in New York. And according to Dewey and Dakin, they would be pointed downward through 1954 if normal cycles existed.[1]

With such "rubber" yardsticks, you're bound to reach wrong conclusions. Figure 9 illustrates what I mean. Here is a budget curve plotted to relate expenses with volume. The dotted line shows what you would get by accepting all dollars as being the same.

The solid line approximates the facts. I have shifted horizontally some of the plotted points. Those above normal, I moved to lower volume equivalents to shrink the inflated dollars. Those below normal, I changed to higher volumes. At reduced prices, they represent larger volumes in terms of *normal* dollars.

A similar effect is hidden in the numerous comparisons drawn as "Per Cent of Sales." Sales prices rarely remain unchanged over long periods of time. Even if they did, the percentages

[1] Dewey, E. R., and E. F. Dakin, "Cycles: The Science of Prediction," p. 187, Henry Holt and Company, Inc., New York, 1949.

would be distorted because of the changing proportions of products sold. These shifts change both material and profit content in a total. So, for my money, sales dollars is perhaps our most misleading yardstick.

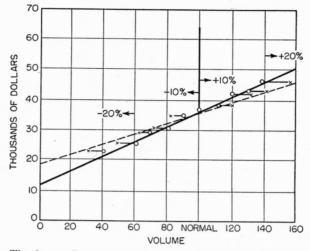

FIG. 9. The heavy line suggests how actual volumes differ from dollar volumes—above normal deflated to offset price increases and below normal inflated to correct for price declines.

MACHINE-HOURS

In trying to get closer to facts, some folks use machine-hours as their measure of work done. In some cases, this yardstick is correct. Such cases occur when you have very high equipment time in relation to man time. An example is where one operator handles dozens of looms or many steam molding presses.

In the usual plant, machine-hours as a denominator is probably in varying degrees about the same as labor dollars. They include all the inefficiencies and buried indirect, plus the variations due to machine vintage. And there is another big variable. If the machine-hours include setup and if either labor dollars or hours would separate this item, machine-hours is more in error.

LABOR DOLLARS

Lots of plants use labor dollars as their yardsticks. That, too, is defective. It includes three variables. First is the obvious one of base rate. Labor dollars used as a divisor produces a burden rate applicable to the average base rate. But we forget this when we figure overhead cost. We multiply the burden rate indiscriminately by low and high base rates.

Work Hours	Base Rate	Labor Dollars	Overhead at 200%
10	$1.00	$10.00	$20.00
10	1.50	15.00	30.00
10	2.00	20.00	40.00

Now you know that the overhead for the $20 of labor is not twice that of the $10. It is not more, simply because the work was done by a $2 per hour man. That is as silly as saying, "We absorb more overhead since we gave a wage increase."

The same thing happens with the second variable, efficiency. Here the error is greater because the range in efficiency is usually greater than it is in base rate. And the less efficient an operation is, the greater the labor dollars and the more overhead we pile on.

You can see in the following figures the importance of this effect:

Standard Minutes per Hour	30	45	60	75	90
Per Cent Efficiency.........	50	75	100	125	150
Labor Costs per 1,000 Std Min at $1.20 per Hour....	$40.00	$26.67	$20.00	$20.00	$20.00

LABOR HOURS

You can avoid the variable of base rate by using labor hours instead of dollars. But you still have the unknowns of efficiency and buried indirect.

Managers make me laugh, inwardly of course, when they talk about stamping timecards for each job. They may even insist that their men report to timekeepers at the end of each job. They overlook completely the errors already included in the exact time stampings. They disregard the fact that their men decide when to ring out. The costs would be just as accurate if their men made out their own time tickets.

Don't get me wrong. I'm not suggesting such a procedure for several reasons. But as far as cost figures are concerned, the operator is the one who makes up the cost in the usual "ring-in–ring-out" setup. All the timekeeper and cost accountant do is to write down the figures. That reminds me of a story Harold Engstrom told me. He said the Shop Superintendent was going round and round with the Cost Accountant. Finally, the "Super" became irked when the cost man implied that his costs were accurate. "Listen," said the Super. "I make the costs. All you do is write 'em down."

Now consider the factor of performance. When it is low, the burden rate is low. When performance improves, the burden rate jumps. Again, as with labor dollars, you make no mistakes with the average. But you do charge too much burden to the poorly performed work. And you charge too little to the efficient operations.

WRONG CHARGING

Let's start with our former example. Here we will call the numerator Dollars, the divisor Hours. Our burden rate comes out to be $1.50 per hour.

$$\frac{\$60,000}{40,000 \text{ hr}} = \$1.50 \text{ per hour}$$

Now we know that all these hours are not at average efficiency. Since some are at different efficiencies, let's make up an example.

Efficiency	Actual Hours	Overhead Charged
140% Ave......	5,000	$ 7,500
120% Ave......	10,000	15,000
Average........	10,000	15,000
80% Ave......	10,000	15,000
60% Ave......	5,000	7,500
	40,000	$60,000

To see the error, let's reconstruct this example. We will correct the actual hours by the performance factor. That will give us a closer measure of the salable work.

Efficiency	Timecard Hours	Actual Production	Overhead Applicable
140% Ave.........	5,000	7,000	$10,500
120% Ave.........	10,000	12,000	18,000
Average..........	10,000	10,000	15,000
80% Ave.........	10,000	8,000	12,000
60% Ave.........	5,000	3,000	4,500
	40,000	40,000	$60,000

Naturally, the amounts shift. They should. The overhead charged was wrong in our first set of figures. The amounts of error in terms of the overhead applicable are as follows:

Efficiency	Overhead			
	Charged	Applicable	Error	Per Cent
140% Ave......	$ 7,500	$10,500	−3,000	−29
120% Ave......	15,000	18,000	−3,000	−17
Average........	15,000	15,000	0	0
80% Ave......	15,000	12,000	+3,000	+25
60% Ave......	7,500	4,500	+3,000	+67

INFLATED DENOMINATOR

Cost charging that is more deceptive is going on every day. It continues in plants where management is too smart to charge the foreman to the job, or pad the man-hour count. Nevertheless, we are holding down the overhead rate and the unabsorbed, even though there is no sleight of hand intended. We hold it down by charging what really is overhead-time cost into our so-called direct labor.

Take two common examples. Delay time is overhead. So is

machine setup. Both of these indirect items, in varying degrees, are often buried in so-called direct labor. We find "unavoidable delays" included even in some standards set by timestudy. Obviously, such items of labor do not represent salable pieces produced. Therefore, they cannot earn any overhead. Yet, when they are included in "direct" labor, the presumption is that overhead is to be applied. And it is.

BURIED OVERHEAD

Let's use some arithmetic. Take 200 per cent as an overhead rate that is easy to work with. This means we apply a $2 overhead charge for each $1 of labor. This form of overhead figuring is the most common, in my experience. Maybe you use it too.

Take an example: Suppose you have $.20 of the hidden kind of indirect in your "direct-labor" dollar. Being indirect, it is

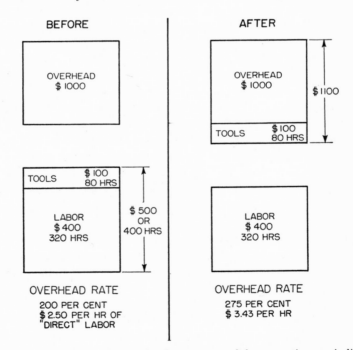

Fig. 10. The change in overhead rates caused by reporting as indirect labor the extra work done by producers when tools are not made.

overhead. Changing it to overhead makes that now equal $2.20. Your labor divisor of $1.00 now becomes $.80. Then your overhead rate is 275 per cent ($2.20/$.80). All we have done is to charge the indirect costs where they belong.

Now hold tight. I want to carry this same example further. It may more nearly represent the case. Suppose other kinds of buried indirect amounting to $.30 bring the total to $.50 of the original dollar of "direct labor." When this is added to overhead, your new total becomes $2.50. Your new "direct labor" yardstick is now $.50. Your new overhead rate then becomes 500 per cent ($2.50/$.50). Another example is shown in Fig. 10.

MIXED DIVISORS

Direct and indirect are mixed up in still other ways. Casting cleaning, heat-treating, packing, painting, and inspection are found in both classes. You might conclude that the operations we find easy to calculate costs for are the ones we class as direct. I have seen evidence that some accountants call those operations direct that the timestudy men can set "rates" for.

On the other side are examples of work reclassified as indirect by supervisors and timestudy men. The transfer is easy to make. All that is necessary is for some part of the work to be shifted from the operator to the trucker or setup man, as examples. Maybe the move is a good one from the standpoint of cost. Perhaps the operator can improve the machine output as a result. Shifting the supplying and the sharpening of tools is in that direction.

You say, "That's right, what are you kicking about?" Surely not about reducing costs. Any progress is OK with me. My quarrel is twofold. First, my basic objection is to all yardsticks that do not measure work output—conversion added. My second objection is to the use of any rubber yardsticks that change with conditions, opinions, and whims.

MEASURED TIME

Of the yardsticks mentioned, none is acceptable. Time comes closest. But the time must be measured. Standard minutes of work, or the equivalent, is the only reliable divisor we have. Even that changes with improvements. So do tonnage, machine-

[handwritten margin note: Basis on how long a part takes to make.]

[handwritten note at bottom: Standard time — What it should take if it is done right way on right machine]

hours, labor dollars, and hours worked. Fortunately, most changes are reductions due to progress.

So to measure our conversion efforts we should use standard time. Then we must get some definitions to separate direct from indirect. Only direct conversion can earn overhead. Take note of the term *earn*. It does not mean the same thing as *apply*. Failure to make this distinction is at the root of some of our errors.

Let's get this problem of overhead rates straight in our minds. "What should be the rate?" is the right question. I'll try to lay the proper foundation for answering that question in the next two chapters.

CHAPTER 5

MANUFACTURING IS CONVERSION

You may lack confidence in your costs. You may say, "They don't hold water." This may happen because results you get differ from what you expected. You feel sure that what one man called "sight value" differs from the cost. You can be wrong, but not always.

You are disappointed, just the same. Your pride is hurt because your judgment appears to be in error. But some is error in figures. The figures can be wrong in several ways. The chief error I want to bring out here is in the overhead applied. To be sure we are together, let's briefly analyze three methods of applying overhead. We will consider these only from the standpoint of manufactured products.

METHOD A—VERY WRONG

In the more old-fashioned method, all overhead and profit are applied to labor plus material. In algebra, it appears as

Price = (Labor + Material) × Manufacturing Overhead × S&A × Profit

We can write this differently to make my point:

Price = (Labor × Overhead × Profit) + (Material × Overhead × Profit)

In this form, you see that all overhead and profit per cents are added to material. This means that the jobs having above-average material content are overcharged.

METHOD B—PARTLY WRONG

The same error occurs to a lesser degree when only sales and administrative overheads are applied to materials. This error is common in industrial estimating. The reason it doesn't show in cost is because sales and administrative expenses are subtracted from "gross profit." The equation of Method B is

Price = (Labor × Overhead × Profit) + (Material × S&A × Profit)

Again, there is a distortion due to material content. You can see that the difference from the first method is only in the relative size of sales and administrative overhead as compared with total overhead. Notice, also, that profit is added to materials in both cases.

HANDLING CHARGE

Before we leave this problem of materials, there is one detail we should touch on. You may contend, and rightly so, that some overhead is chargeable to materials. The figure often mentioned is "10 per cent for handling." I know of instances where 10 per cent is about right. By and large, however, that amount isn't even an educated guess. If you insist upon some "handling charge," find out what it is. If you determine proper figures, you will find that

1. One percentage does not apply to all materials.
2. Any percentage is not a function of the material cost except as you figure it that way.
3. Some percentage return on capital invested is logical, but it will not resemble the 20 to 40 per cent often added as S&A.

Also, if you work out factors to cover "material handling," be sure to distinguish between raw and finished purchases. You may spend only one-tenth as much per dollar in buying a motor as a bar of steel. Watch your step in classifying motors and lock washers in the same group of purchased materials. My personal experience has been to skip the handling charge.

METHOD C—CORRECT

To escape distortions, you should keep materials separated. Said the other way, you should apply all overhead and profit to labor. Labor measures the work added. It is the conversion that you apply to change materials to those products desired by your customers. This method expressed like the previous two would be

$$\text{Price} = (\text{Labor} \times \text{Overhead} \times \text{Profit}) + \text{Material}$$

METHOD COMPARISONS

Now let's see how these methods would apply to examples of your products. And to keep this simple, I will use labor dollars when I should use standard time. Suppose we have only three different products. Assume that their labor and material costs are:

	Product X	Product Y	Product Z
Labor.........	$25,000	$ 50,000	$25,000
Material.......	10,000	50,000	40,000
	$35,000	$100,000	$65,000

Now let's take your manufacturing overhead as $200,000 with S&A burden of $50,000. Suppose a profit of $50,000. Under Method A, you would distribute all overhead and profit equal to $300,000 over the base cost of $200,000. Then the results would look like:

	Product X	Product Y	Product Z
Labor: $100,000.......	$25,000	$ 50,000	$ 25,000
Material: 100,000.......	10,000	50,000	40,000
Base Cost.............	$35,000	$100,000	$ 65,000
Mfg. OH: $200,000.......	$35,000	$100,000	$ 65,000
S&A: 50,000.......	8,750	25,000	16,250
Profit: 50,000.......	8,750	25,000	16,250
Price................	$87,500	$250,000	$162,500

Under Method B, you would apply manufacturing overhead to labor. Sales and administrative and profit would be applied to manufacturing cost.

	Product X	Product Y	Product Z
Labor: $100,000.......	$ 25,000	$ 50,000	$ 25,000
Mfg. OH: 200,000.......	50,000	100,000	50,000
Material: 100,000.......	10,000	50,000	40,000
Manufactured Cost......	$ 85,000	$200,000	$115,000
S&A: $50,000.......	$ 10,625	$ 25,000	$ 14,375
Profit: 50,000.......	10,625	25,000	14,375
Price..................	$106,250	$250,000	$143,750

Going on to Method C, you would apply all overheads and profit to labor only.

	Product X	Product Y	Product Z
Labor: $100,000.......	$ 25,000	$ 50,000	$ 25,000
Mfg. OH: 200,000.......	50,000	100,000	50,000
S&A: 50,000.......	12,500	25,000	12,500
Profit: 50,000.......	12,500	25,000	12,500
Conversion............	$100,000	$200,000	$100,000
Material: $100,000.......	$ 10,000	$ 50,000	$ 40,000
Price..................	$110,000	$250,000	$140,000

PER CENT DISTORTIONS

Let's compare answers by using Method C as a base. First, note how the sales prices vary.

Method	Product X	%	Product Y	%	Product Z	%
A	$ 87,500	80	$250,000	100	$162,500	116
B	106,250	96	250,000	100	143,750	103
C	110,000	100	250,000	100	140,000	100

Observe that the price of Product Y is the same in all three instances. I put this one in to show that the *average* product cost or price comes out the same by any method of figuring. But the whole point of my discussion is that we get wrong answers for all the not-average products.

Next, let's compare the profits in the usual way—per cent of sales dollars.

Method	Product X	%	Product Y	%	Product Z	%
A..........	$ 8,750	8.8	$ 25,000	12.5	$ 16,250	16.3
B..........	10,625	10.6	25,000	12.5	14,375	14.4
C..........	12,500	12.5	25,000	12.5	12,500	12.5
Conversion C	100,000	...	200,000	...	100,000	

Of course, the profit on all three products is the same per cent in Method C. That's the way we figured it. That is the way it should be computed, in my opinion.

Let me try to clinch this business of material distortion. Suppose you run a big pickle factory. You use steel tank cars to transport acetic acid. Years ago, you found out that your customers didn't like iron-flavored pickles. Ever since, you have had a rubber converter put a lining on the inside. One day, you needed three tank cars in a hurry. So you telephoned your rubber-company friends to quote a price on lining three cars they agreed to buy for you from the car builder near their plant. When you saw the quotation, you hit the roof. Your supplier had tacked 33 per cent S&A onto the price of the tank cars.

MIXED PRODUCTS

You can see similarities in the foregoing examples to products of your own plant. Your line of products may have an even wider range in proportions of labor to material. All I'm trying to show is how the cost or price you come up with is affected by the "formula" you use.

Keep in mind that these examples are only different arrangements of the same figures. They do not add or omit any overhead and profit. They show only the effects of arithmetic.

That's what fools us. One author says, "We should consider the business as a whole." Another says, "We can't be so far wrong. Our profit record is better than average."

This "average" thinking is dangerous. You know as well as I do that you will get the wrong answer if you substitute an incorrect factor in a formula. And while my analogy may be a poor one, we must analyze consistently. We argue that, "Our business is different," "Ours is a job shop," "We make lots of nonstandard products." Therefore, I say you cannot get the right answers by an average method of costing.

AVERAGE COSTS

Take a look at the condition that existed in the other fellow's plant. His was the average method of costing. Some of his

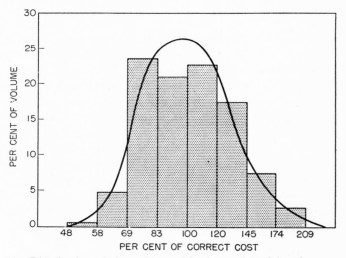

Fig. 11. Distribution of the volume of business plotted by the per cents of correct costs that previous costing methods had distorted.

costs were as low as 52 per cent of correct. Overcosting ran as high as 109 per cent. The whole range is shown in Fig. 11. If you can get the laws of chance to cooperate with you, you will have 68 per cent of your business around the average. But 28 per cent will be off quite a bit. And 4 per cent will be way off (Fig. 12).

What you have to keep in mind, however, is that a progressive outfit is changing all the time. You may have a minor change in one line and a major shift in another. One product becomes more popular, another falls off. Whether you notice these shifts

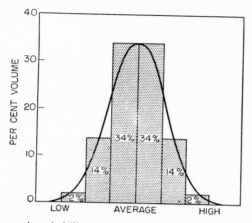

Fɪɢ. 12. The usual probability curve that suggests what you might expect to find in amount of incorrect costing when you break down some average overhead method.

or not, the average no longer holds true. You are faced with a choice.

1. "Let's go ahead on the same basis. The error is small."
2. "Let's revise our burden rates. The shift is real."

Both are wrong. In either choice, an average is continued. **If** you subdivide it, you can approach the control you need.

> *The costing method should automatically*
> *correct for changes in the product mix.*

That is the direction I am heading for in this book.

WHAT IS CONVERSION?

Do you use some basic item like cast iron? If so, your castings started as iron ore somebody dug out of a hill in Minnesota. It was hauled by boat from Superior to Cleveland. Republic may have converted it to pig iron. Then the Pennsy hauled it to your supply foundry. They melted it again and molded the shapes you wanted. And a truck delivered the castings to you.

1. The miner converted the hill to ore.
   He added conversion and profit.
   Shipping and profit raised the cost.
2. The steelmaker converted the ore to pig iron.
   He added conversion and profit.
   Freight and profit raised the cost.
3. The foundryman converted pig iron to your castings.
   He added conversion and profit.
   Trucking and profit raised the cost.

You will add conversion and profit to change the castings into shapes your customers want. This work of changing material to make a desired product is conversion. You convert starting materials into salable products. You apply the skills and abilities of your organization to the process of converting.

You design, manufacture, and sell. You use tools, equipment, and plant. You pay wages, taxes, and charges. You add profit. All these are caused by your work of conversion. If you made any one of the previous conversions cited, your costs would be different. Your work would be different. So would your plant and equipment, your skills and abilities.

CONVERSION COSTS

Therefore, I submit that your costs, all of them, grow out of the conversions you make. You can see those costs in the casting example (Fig. 13). That is simple in comparison with your production and distribution. Chances are you have thousands of parts. Perhaps, you make several products. For that reason, you must have several different conversion costs. Your different products require different skills, equipment, and maybe different sales methods. Your different conversion costs may not be apparent at first glance. They are there, just the same.

Now don't get lost. I'm not talking about labor and material costs. You already have those. They may be figured out to the fourth decimal place. It's overhead I'm worried about. Spreading burden with a shovel is where we make our big mistakes. You can see different overheads in the casting example. You could see yours more distinctly if each of your products were made in a separate plant. Having all your products under one roof does not alter the fact of difference. It only makes a problem of analysis to get the several correct overhead rates.

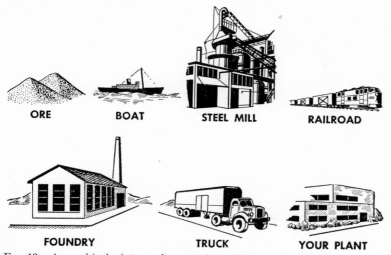

Fig. 13. A graphical picture of conversion of iron ore to castings, a commonly understood process that differs only in degree from what we do in all manufacturing.

MIXING RATES

You may say, "We get the separation with departmental or machine-hour rates." These cannot give the right answers. Here's why.

Remember my example of varied machine rates in Chap. 3? Such variations would not concern us if each product were completed by one or several departments. That is not usual. Here is error No. 1. The more common and probably greater error is in spreading the overhead above the department or the machine. Production control, accounting, engineering, and other overheads are spread to the department or machine on what basis? "Uniform" is the usual answer.

We know these are not uniformly caused. Small quantities take more production control, accounting, and timestudy than large quantities. Specials take more engineering, purchasing, and production control than standard items. And so on.

"REPRORATED REPRORATIONS"

Again you may object, "But we overcome this error by using cost centers. We know the full cost of our overhead departments. We charge those departments using the services according to

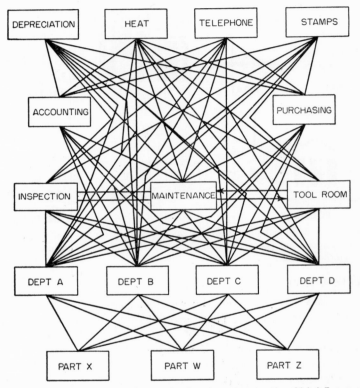

Fig. 14. See if you can understand what happens to the Chief Inspector in the maze of reprorated reprorations.

their demands. Therefore, we get the right amounts into the right places."

That all sounds nice. But it doesn't hold water. First, it can't be done correctly except in part. Engineering and similar service charges cannot be correctly applied this way. Services like time-study and accounting are more related to parts and product than to machine-hours or to shop departments. Then and more important, you lose control of allocated expenses. If the end cost goes up or down, you have a helluva time finding out why. "Costs are divided, allocated, reallocated and merged until components are no longer accessible for managerial planning and control." [1]

Here's a case we ran into. A CPA named Jack Wayne insisted that departmental rates be used. By his method, each department was charged with all expenses assignable to it, service and shop departments. Curiosity as to how this worked out led us to trace through the prorations. We found that the Chief Inspector, as an example, finally came to rest only after 37 "reprorated reprorations." See if you can find what happened to him with the aid of Fig. 14. This is simplified, believe it or not. Imagine all the cross charges not shown that occur between service departments. No wonder managers get lost.

Sure, this cross charging shows the total "cost" of service centers. But such costs are only informatory. You can get such figures any time you need them. Why carry them on daily as part of a "cost system"?

FLOW PROCESS

Why not use a direct approach? Why not charge indirect costs directly to your products? They have to get there in the final analysis. Only products that go out the door and stay out can earn overhead. Overhead departments cannot.

Let me try to simplify this mix-up. We begin with the fact that your products flow through processes. Some are better equipped than others. Some are more costly. Some take a lot more service attention. And remember, I see no distinction between making and selling your products in thinking of processes.

All the steps to make and sell a product are part of the cost of the particular process it goes through. The process causes the conversion cost. Several products may go through the same process. Therefore, they have the same conversion cost.

CORRECT OVERHEAD

To get correct overheads, we must analyze what takes place. First, we analyze the products to determine what processes are

[1] Goetz, Billy E., The Role of Costs in Managerial Planning and Control, SAM Publication 27, Chicago Chapter, 1947.

used to complete them. Next, we should find out how much productive standard time is required to make these products. This gives us the proper divisors. Then, we analyze the expenses caused by those processes. This way, we get the overhead that is necessary to get the work done. As a result, we establish the proper numerators for our burden rates. Dividing correct expense groups by their correct work divisors will give us the answers we seek.

There are several steps in the analysis. All are simple even though they do take some detailed work. Most have to do with the overhead breakdown. We will go through these steps progressively in chapters that follow. To avoid detours, we will discuss first the correct divisors—our measures of work done—in our next chapter.

CHAPTER 6

WHAT MEASURES SALABLE PIECES?

"Why are we in business?" One answer is to make profit. Another is to render service. To render service at a profit, we convert materials into products that customers want. The work of conversion is what we call productive labor. All the other costs result from that. All the equipment and staff are built around the conversion process. In simple terms, overhead is a rental charge applied for the time our skills and tools are used.

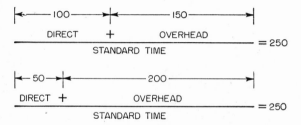

FIG. 15. With both direct labor and overhead in the "rate," there is no confusion when one goes up as the other is reduced.

But we get mixed up in our thinking. We went through, "Your overhead is too high" in Chap. 3. I tried to show there how misleading ratios can be. Now I want to ask, "Why separate labor from overhead?" If both were together in the numerator, we could see more clearly the interrelations.

If both were in one rate, it wouldn't bother us when one went up as the other decreased. Actually, that is the way most folks compute costs. They calculate direct labor costs by extending time by wage rate. Then they multiply the dollar result by an overhead rate. Why make two calculations, or dozens as those do who use machine-hour rates? Look at the diagram, Fig. 15. You can see that it makes no difference whether cost goes in direct or in overhead. Only the separation causes us confusion. It is the total we must watch.

STANDARD-TIME DIVISOR

Notice also that I show *standard time* as the divisor. That is what you have to use if you are going to escape the errors of rubber yardsticks. You need a measure of work that is distinctly separated from the rate of compensation. Wage rates are subject to change every time "the calendar turns one revolution." Oftener, if there is a "reopening clause" in the contract.

Wages are determined by economic conditions and negotiations. On the other hand, work measurement is something distinctly different. There should be but one fair standard time for performing a given operation in a specified manner. This standard should be built from valid timestudy observations. It cannot be a fair measure of work done if it is juggled in any way to offset inequities in base wages.[1]

STANDARD TIME

I think that the standard-time denominator is the most useful contribution made to industry by the timestudy man. However, its value is lost in many plants because we cling to dollar yardsticks. Maybe the continuing shrinkage of dollar values will force us to see the advantages of standard time as a measure. Of course, as labor costs jump skyward, they absorb more overhead—or do they?

Standard time is the correct basis for overhead computations, because it is not affected by either wage rates or performance efficiencies. It is correct, also, because industrial operations are conversion processes that use the equipment and skills of your organization for specific lengths of time. These time elements are best measured by the standards set for incentives. Time in manufacturing is basic to sound overhead costing. Time has not yet been diluted by the politicians in Washington. Time is important because it is the chief factor in labor cost. "Time standards measuring the direct labor performance of a product or part immediately become the prime factor in all financial controls." [2]

[1] Carroll, Phil, "Should Incentives for Employees Be Preserved?" University of Michigan, Conferences on Industrial Relations, 1946–1947.

[2] Voitsberger, D. M., Standard Costs and Cost Standards, *Modern Management,* August, 1945.

Beside these major uses, the standard-time denominator is essential in comparisons of plant, department, and employee performances. It is useful in the operation of budget control. It greatly simplifies computations of inventory. And, believe it or not, some companies compute their monthly operating statements on the basis of standard times.

COMMON DENOMINATOR

Standard times come closest to being the ideal common denominator. Why is this so important to business? "It is because manufacture, in general, is very complicated. If it were simple enough, the product itself could become the denominator. Take, for example, the manufacturer of cement. If all of the output of a cement plant were shipped in one size of bag, then the bag of cement itself would become the perfect denominator. All labor, expense, and profit could be expressed in terms of 'bags of cement.'

"Even in this simple manufacturing operation, simple from the standpoint of costing, the addition of a line of barrels of cement destroys the product as a denominator. Costs can no longer be expressed in terms of a unit of shipment. The unit of shipment is no longer a unit of measure. . . . It is hard to conceive of a business so simple that the product can be effectively used as a denominator. The only one I think of that might fall in this class is the specialty baker who makes only one size loaf of bread. Because of the nature of his product, he has to ship everything that he makes every day. He has no inventory in process. But let the baker add a line of rolls, then his cost system is destroyed." [3]

WHAT IS PRODUCTIVE?

When you turn out more than one product, you need some universal measure of output. Most measures break down because they differ from one product to the next. This is not true of standard time per piece. Timestudy standards used for wage-incentive purposes furnish the one way to measure a total of work done.

[3] Wallace, Bruce, Time Standards in Costing, *SAM Industrial Engineer,* January, 1944.

However, a true standard-time measure of production cannot include irregularities such as extra work and other indirect labor. The measurement of output must consist only of productive efforts. Some work now called indirect would more properly be classified as productive. A practical working definition of productive labor might read as follows:

> *Productive operations are those performed regularly to each piece. "Regularly" can be interpreted to mean stated percentages, as with inspection.*

Under that definition you can include certain types of inspection, packing, painting, casting cleaning, and similar work. Transferring such direct operations from overhead to productive labor permits you to gain much better control. It reduces the amount of overhead to be spread over direct labor. Hence, it helps you get more correct product costs. Making your denominator larger reduces errors in overhead application.

PRODUCTIVE STANDARDS

You may think of standard time as Standard Hours. I prefer standard minutes. They involve only half as many decimal places. You may have heard standard minutes called "Bs," "Norms," "Manits," "Points," or "Units." I use the term "Unit" to avoid confusing measured time with clock time.

PURE UNITS

All Units produced must be properly accounted for if they are to become the conversion part of inventory. If more pieces than good finished parts are reported, there is inflation. If extra operations are performed because of faulty material, they are variations from standard. They can be correctly reflected in cost only when reported as indirect Expense Units. Obviously, it is very important that the Unit denominator be kept free from dilution. Any inflation will cause your costs to appear lower and inventory higher. Also any inflation in Units will cause an apparent overabsorption of overhead expenses.

INCOMPLETE COVERAGE

To have a reliable denominator, you must have all productive work measured. You cannot set standards for the easy jobs and

Wealth is labor - time -; use Time STANDARD

pass up the difficult work. If you do, your denominator is a mixture of grass and hay. You must add the unknown quantity of "daywork" to the measured standard time. Daywork must be converted by some arbitrary factor like 50 per cent. Be sure to lean toward the conservative. Remember what I just said about inflation.

This is similar to the problem we frequently encounter in wage-incentive installation. From the time the first department goes on incentive, we have at least two denominators for overhead. The difference between them can be great. You have a tulip and paving-brick mixture of labor measurements regardless of what you call labor. You try to set two denominators that are the equivalents of each other. Naturally, if volume remained constant throughout, you would have

$$\text{Old Labor} \times \text{Old Burden} = \text{New Labor} \times \text{New Burden}$$

If new conditions do not approximate the old, you have considerable over- or underabsorption unless you change burden rates to correspond.

COMPLETE MEASUREMENT

The best way I know to get your total denominator measured is by means of standard data. It is better than the direct time-study method under every condition I can remember. It is the correct and practical method to use when cost control is your objective.

From your point of view, the most important advantage is economy. I place economy first because practically all operations must be measured to know what your production actually is. You need a sound common denominator. You need complete coverage. While you might get coverage by timestudy, your chances are better with the less expensive method.

Second, standard data permits you to set standards before work starts. That gives you a twofold advantage. Obviously, it enables you economically to

1. Measure small lots and starts of large orders for new work.
2. Estimate for quotations, suggestion awards, and most types of method-improvement proposals.

EXTRA WORK

Third is an advantage very critical in cost control. But it is not inherent. You must insist upon it. This has to do with what I call "purity," for lack of a better term, of your productive-work denominator.

I'll try to make my point with an illustration. You are about to set a standard for machining a casting. It could go on a Warner & Swasey or on a Potter & Johnston lathe. Suppose the W & S standard to be 10 minutes, the P & J to be 5 minutes. If you do not follow a rule, you will get both types of standards. You don't want that condition. Ten minutes represents twice the labor and overhead in inventory in terms of 5 minutes. You must follow a principle like, "standards shall be set for the best methods and conditions we have available in our shop."

When you follow such a rule, standards set in advance have two by-products important in cost control. One is the greater tendency to set standards *for conditions as they should be.* The other is the more probable separation from the "pure standard" of all allowances made to the operators for nonstandard conditions. These consist of extra work done, as in our example of the Warner & Swasey job. Also, working conditions, materials, and workmanship.

CONSISTENT STANDARDS

Fourth is consistency. This, and at least two other advantages I could cite, are vital in employee acceptance and job satisfaction. All are important in cost control. As I say elsewhere,[4] "If employees do not make substantial premium earnings, the incentive plan is not a success." Obviously, the standards must be effective. Otherwise, they are of little value in cost control. We will discuss this phase in Chap. 22.

Here we should think of consistency as it is related to "purity" —the third advantage just described. With "pure" consistent standards, your work measurements represent good, salable pieces.

[4] Carroll, Phil, "Timestudy for Cost Control," McGraw-Hill Book Company, Inc., New York, 1943. Carroll, Phil, "Timestudy Fundamentals for Foremen," McGraw-Hill Book Company, Inc., New York, 1943.

EXTRA LABOR COSTS

Earlier I said that extra work was not direct production. Of course, necessary work must be paid for. Extra allowances should be made when the extras occur. This is the only fair method. It is the one method that calls attention to the extra costs. Take waiting time as a better understood example. If it is buried in work standards, it must be allowed as an average time. The man on incentive "takes the bitter with the sweet." On the other hand, when no delay time is included, he calls for it as it occurs. Then everyone is made aware of the lost time. Something may be done to control the amount, when waiting time is reported separately. Nothing is done when we bury it in work standards.

The same applies to extras caused by faulty materials or non-standard conditions and setups. The latter are very important in the job shops. All these extras should be measured and kept separate. And they should be on incentive. Such work should not be covered by daywork allowances. "Daywork" is too often classified as productive labor when actually it is mostly indirect.

NO TEMPORARY STANDARDS

Perhaps the basic fundamental I'm trying to emphasize will be more clearly seen from another example. You are acquainted with what some call "temporary" standards. What makes them temporary? Usually, it is some off-color condition. Maybe the stock is too heavy, the holes are too small, or the burrs are too thick. Extra work is required to get the pieces into line with your "specs."

The extra work is exactly the same type of wasted effort as if the pieces had to be reworked because of prior defective workmanship. If such extra work were called rework, you would classify it as indirect. Regardless, the extra work does not add any pieces to your output. As a consequence, you cannot logically call it direct labor. Such extra work cannot earn overhead.

All such extra work should be separated from the standard work by the timestudy man. Said the other way, he should not add extra work to regular work in one total classified as "direct labor." To solve the problem, you need to distinguish between pure production and any extras made necessary by current conditions. Only by excluding the extras can you avoid inflating

Your measure of productive work.
Your apparent overhead absorption.
Your inventory evaluation.

SETUP TIME

Setup is another item that is sometimes mixed in with what we call direct. It may even be buried in the incentive "rate." That is wrong. The "rate" is unfair to the man for quantities less than average. It is unfair to the company for quantities greater than average.

But from our point here, we do not get good pieces for the setup time. Therefore, it is indirect. One man said, "But you can't get any pieces unless you do setup. Setup is absolutely necessary." I agreed and added, "So are the works manager, foreman, engineer, and inspector. That doesn't make them direct labor."

The other day at lunch a client asked, "When will you have the setup men on standard?" He was concerned with the cost of setup. He said an increasing amount of specials and spare parts was creating a concealed loss. He was right. His overhead was spread as an average. It was incorrectly applying extra setups to work that had relatively little.

TOOLING COST

Similar to extra operations and setups is another indirect time usually buried in direct. This one is very subtle. But it is often larger than the inflations previously discussed. It may cause more error too, as you will see.

To illustrate, let's assume that our plant manufactures two like products. Gadgets are made in large quantities, Widgits in small lots. Naturally, our large-volume product is tooled up. Let us assume that the tools cost $250. Now, we agree that tools are overhead. And we made them because we figured our labor cost would come down faster than our overhead went up.

At the risk of boring you, let me repeat that we deliberately raised our overhead cost by making the tools. Even though these were charged off currently, the overhead rate was increased temporarily. In addition, we made the tools with the planned purpose of reducing our labor cost. This reduced our direct-labor divisor and further increased our overhead rate. Only if total production expanded would this rise in burden rate be offset.

With tools, we have a lower standard time. Let's assume that the standard for Gadgets is 1.0 minute per piece. For Widgits, without tools, suppose that the standard time is 2.0 minutes each. Point No. 1 is that the extra minute (2.0 − 1.0) allowed to make Widgits is not direct labor. It is tool cost, spent as labor because that method is cheaper. But it is tool cost and therefore overhead.

OVERHEAD MISAPPLICATION

Do not assume that I am quibbling over details. See what happens when you apply overhead by the usual accounting methods. To explain, let's figure on making 10,000 Gadgets and 1,000 Widgits. The ordinary accounting procedure would extend and add labor costs to get current output. At $1.50 an hour, each minute has a cost of $.025. So our labor cost for Gadgets would be 10,000 × 1.0 min × $.025, or $250.00. For Widgits, it would be $50.00 (1,000 × 2.0 × $.025). Our total labor cost for Gadgets and Widgits then is $300.00.

We will neglect all other items of overhead costs to see what happens to the tool costs. We spent $250 for tooling Gadgets. We spent nothing to tool up the Widgits. In our example then, overhead equals our tool costs of $250 plus 0. Our overhead rate becomes

$$\frac{\$250 + 0}{\$300} = 83\frac{1}{3}\%$$

Going on in the regular way to calculate cost, we apply 83⅓ per cent overhead to the labor cost. For Widgits, that would equal $41.67 ($50.00 × 83⅓%) for overhead. If we charge $41.67 of our tool cost to Widgits, then only $208.33 is charged to Gadgets. But we spent $250.00. That was our starting premise.

CORRECT TOOL COST

Figuring correctly, we should charge the extra 1.0 minute (2.0 − 1.0) of work done on Widgits to overhead. It is labor cost substituted for tooling. Then our arithmetic would be as follows:

$$\frac{\$250.00 + \$.025(1,000 \times 1.0)}{\$.025(10,000 \times 1.0 + 1,000 \times 1.0)} = \frac{\$275.00}{\$275.00} = 100\%$$

Now look what happens when we apply overhead to our two products manufactured by different methods. With 100 per cent as our overhead rate, the amount charged for tools to Widgits is $25 (Labor cost of $25 $\times$ 100%). The amount charged to Gadgets is $250 Labor $\times$ 100 per cent, or $250. This $250 is the tool cost we spent for Gadgets. Both new charges are correct. We have not charged tool cost to the product that was not tooled. Obviously too, we would not load all the other overhead costs onto the 1.0 minute of indirect labor a "temporary standard" would bury in the direct.

I'll readily admit that this example was rigged to make it come out right. My purpose is to illustrate the two errors: (1) misapplication of overhead, and (2) incorrect costs. Yet, I should add that only a specially set up example could come out even. The fact is that we make tools when their costs are less than the labor savings. Hence usual equations could not be expected to balance.

When I spoke about this misplacement of tooling cost before the Newark Chapter of NACA, an accountant raised this question. "How are you going to set the right price on your products if you put all that kind of direct labor in your overhead?"

First, as I've tried to show, you can't get the right cost as we now figure it. Second, as a rule, we set prices on a line of products. Third, we often set prices in relation to competition and disregard cost. Even so, we can never find out where our profits are unless we first get cost facts.

INFLATED DIVISOR

You can say, "You're making mountains out of molehills." You are right except that you cannot gain control of costs when you misrepresent them. I think that we have to show these irregularities separately. My belief is that we have to get them out in the open so that we can work to reduce the variations.

Most important here, including such extras will inflate the divisor you use to compute overhead rates. And what is more misleading, you come back later and apply overhead to these hidden extras. That wouldn't be so bad, if it were not for the fact that, in so doing, you undercost the more correctly processed products.

Consider what may be true of your plant. John Nickerson reports improvements in production resulting from incentives that

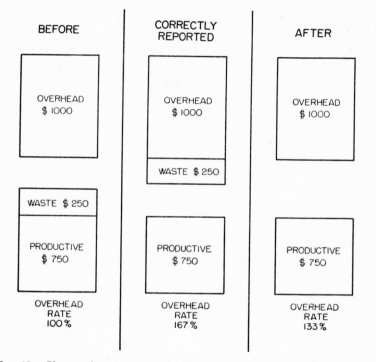

Fig. 16. Observe how correct reporting raises your overhead "rate" and how it continues higher even after you reduce waste time by any better management method.

range from 0 to 103 per cent.[5] Parts of the increases were paid out as added earnings. At the same time, there were eliminations of waste time like waiting for work and extra operations.

If we assume that waste costs buried in direct labor amount to 25 per cent, just to illustrate, you can see what happens to overhead rates when they are reported correctly (Fig. 16). This

[5] Wage Incentive Plans, Management Consultant Division, War Production Board, October, 1944.

takes place when you introduce good timestudy. It isn't timestudy that raises the overhead. It is the correction of reporting. "You call a spade a spade."

Finally, amounts added to standards by arbitrators or by compromises are not equivalent to added production. They cannot earn overhead. Therefore, these amounts too are expense units.

SALABLE PIECES

Standard time is the best measure we have of salable pieces. But we have to be careful in reporting. If we could use bags of cement as Bruce Wallace did, we could not get mixed up. Both overhead and labor would be in the numerator. Putting both together overcomes only our confusion about overhead rates. We still have to have the correct standard-time divisor.

In my first book, "Timestudy for Cost Control," I tried to lay the foundation for sound work measurement. My purpose was to explain how to establish a common denominator that correctly measures the actual output. Actual output is good, salable pieces that the customer pays for and does not return.

Getting standard time to represent good, salable pieces takes only a clear understanding. First, you should clearly define *productive*. Then you should make sure that your timestudy men know what the definition means. They must have basic standards for methods to be able to recognize nonstandard conditions. They should separate everything that is not productive when they set the standards. My belief is that only the timestudy men can set up the proper measure of salable pieces.

CHAPTER 7

HOW TO ANALYZE YOUR OVERHEAD

Dr. Lillian M. Gilbreth says, "Too often, a so-called final answer to a question continues to be accepted long after the question itself has changed."[1] You may call this inertia. Perhaps you prefer "resistance to change." Edward C. Schleh says, "We follow the leader."[2] We adopt a management tool because others use it. We decide against it because others don't use some more advanced method. All this taken together means there can be no progress until somebody breaks through the barrier.

COSTING METHOD

Your position may be, "Our competitors figure costs the same as we do," or "We use the method set up by our trade association." But think. Are you trying to justify past practices? Ask yourself the question, "How does our customer look at our price?" If he can produce the things he buys from you, he will figure costs by his methods, not yours.

You have such personal reactions yourself sometimes. You say, "That don't look like ten dollars' worth to me." You have six other places you can use a ten spot. But if you need the article, you plan to

1. Seek a substitute, or
2. Make it yourself.

If your customer uses the same reasoning, you lose the sale. The price could be too high because of your method of figuring. But remember, when you lose sales on the high side of the average, you raise the average cost of the remaining business. Like-

[1] Gilbreth, Dr. Lillian M., Points for Emphasis in Modern Office Management, *Proceedings NOMA,* 1951.

[2] Schleh, Edward C., Why Follow the Leader?, *Management Review,* p. 106, March, 1951.

wise, you are apt to get the business in those products that are underpriced by the average method of figuring.

To make bad matters worse, your overhead costs are high and rising. They go up automatically with methods improvement. The trend is inescapable as you continue to install better tools, designs, and methods. It goes up when you add hospitalization, pension plan, more holidays, and more clerks to figure these things out. It goes higher when you add new equipment and buildings. And still higher when you improve industrial relations, quality control, planning, and cost controls.

YESTERDAY   TODAY   TOMORROW

Fɪɢ. 17.   Each day we progress, we narrow the base for overhead appli cation.   In so doing, we exaggerate the errors in our overhead costs.

Our concern here is not that these improvements may be both practical and economical. We will assume that they are. It is that each day of progress narrows the base of overhead application. It increases the probability of error in overhead costing (Fig. 17).

DON'T BACK AWAY

Merwin P. Cass, past president of the Newark Chapter of NACA, said in May, 1951: "Management will usually understand 'bogeys' for labor and standards for material. But when the subject of overhead comes up, management is prone to take the easy way out and guess that very little can be done about overhead costs. Management seems to think of overhead expenses as over-the-head costs."

But you cannot dodge the problem that way. You are forced to make decisions in order to progress. Many are what I call "crystal-ball gazing." Projections must be made into the future. The question is, "What will happen if we follow this course of action?"

To predict with reasonable accuracy, you need correct costs. Important also is your need to know the relation between volume and expense. Knowing what your expenses should be at a given business level is very essential. It is vital in making certain policy decisions and thus in the control of your operations.

You can partly answer such questions after you have analyzed expenses to prepare variable budgets. You need to know also what your conversion costs are by lines of products.

To my way of thinking, knowledge of the correct costs of conversion is vital in the successful conduct of multiproduct businesses. Conversion costing provides the only way I know to get overhead expenses charged to the processes that cause them. To get to such costs, our first step is to analyze our overhead expenses.

TWO KEYSTONES

We want to make our analyses so that they will give us two important keystones for our foundation. These are

1. *Expense.* What are expenses likely to be for specific conditions and volumes of business?

2. *Control.* Who are the men to be held accountable for controlling the expenses to the predictions?

Predicting expenses in a general way is what we ordinarily call budgeting. And if we have the "makin's" for good budgeting, we should be able to make predictions of expenses for specific conditions. Hence, one step in our process is to find out what happens to expenses with changes in volume of sales or production.

But saying in advance that expenses for a given condition will be "so much" is the easier part. Will they, when you check your results? That is the measurement part. It is the more important part too. If the predictions are not borne out, then you wonder

Was the decision a sound one?
Were the expenses predicted correctly?

Did actual expenses meet predictions?

Did those responsible control costs?

Since control is the basic objective you are after, you must set up accountability for results that are built into your predictions. Then you must compare expenses with predictions by responsibilities for their control.

WHO IS RESPONSIBLE?

Fixing responsibilities to specific individuals is similar to breaking up group wage incentive and applying work measurement to individual men. It must be done if you are to have accountability. "Accountability is a requirement under which each member of the organization renders a report on his discharge of responsibilities and is judged fairly on the basis of his record of accomplishment." [3]

To gain control of expenses, you must set up four conditions. I like to add a fifth.

1. Fix accountability by individuals.
2. Know what the expenses should be.
3. Compare actuals with predictions.
4. Take the action indicated.
5. Pay incentive according to results.

ORGANIZATIONAL CHANGES

You start by lining up expenses according to present responsibilities. This step is important. The point is that maybe last year some function reported to the Vice-President. Now it is under the Controller, and 5 years ago it was charged to the Works Manager. When you think of the people responsible, you are looking at the organization as it exists. It was not that way yesterday, was it? "No. Joe Smith had only Sales Promotion. Now he's head of Advertising."

Maybe that change did not split or combine expenses. But many changes do. Responsibilities are rearranged often, in a progressive concern. And that makes a problem in overhead analysis.

[3] Davis, Ralph C., "The Fundamentals of Top Management," p. 320, Harper & Brothers, New York, 1951.

Billy Goetz states what not to do in a few words. "And we never chop up and allocate the superintendent's salary to the departments under him. . . . This again largely avoids the clerical work wrapped up in the fictions of allocations." [4]

If you have been allocating expenses, your situation may be like that reported by the National Industrial Conference Board. "It was found at the start of the budget installation that the company had many classes of expenditure for which nobody in particular accepted any responsibility." [5]

I fully realize that some men do not "accept responsibilities" regardless of accounting. That is failure to execute. The responsibility lies with their superiors. Let's line up the expense accounting with the organizational lines of responsibility. Let's keep together all the expenses under the control of an individual. Let's not mix in any expenses someone else should control.

BUILDING MEN

De Voitsberger says, "The underlying principle of cost control is that definite responsibility must be established for accomplishments." [6] And item No. 1 in a brochure by Koppers Company is "To divide the total responsibility into logical assignments." [7]

All this is only good organization. We all know that. But how will we develop competent men unless we measure their performance? How do they develop without measures of their accomplishments? How can they develop if they are not trained to meet standards of performance?

Of course, to measure fairly you must define the job to be done for the expense assigned. This we rarely do. The result is that supervisors in most overhead positions cut out their work to suit their own abilities. Important functions go on day after day largely by momentum. No one has been given the job to look after them. Maybe they are on the border line between assigned

[4] Goetz, Billy E., Role of Costs in Managerial Planning and Control, SAM Publication 27, Chicago Chapter, 1947.

[5] Budgetary Control in Manufacturing Industry, National Industrial Conference Board, New York, 1931.

[6] Voitsberger, D. M., Standard Costs and Cost Standards, *Modern Management,* August, 1945.

[7] The Control Section—A New Aid to Management, adopted from a brochure of the Koppers Company of Pittsburgh, *Modern Management,* October, 1949.

functions. They hang in the air because the men responsible for adjacent functions are too willing "to leave well enough alone." Not only must you assign all functions and measure performances, you have to coach those responsible so that they perform as members of the team. Each is like a link in a chain. And you know the old saying, "A chain can be no stronger than its weakest link."

Only people can control—take action. Hence, we must know who is supposed to take the action. And we must follow up to see that the work was done completely and correctly. So we want to set up our expenses to conform with accountability.

ANALYZING ACCOUNTS

Make sure that expenses recorded by account number contain all the money spent for that function. You may find that certain accounts do not represent the whole total of the expense. As an example, you may find that some people responsible for staff departments are charged into a general supervisory account. Your company is different, I know. You do not have such things as secret payrolls. But you have heard of concerns that pay certain people from the New York office.

In one plant, a number of office expenses were plotted from salaries recorded on the payroll. Curves were drawn. Budgets were set up. They were applied before it was discovered that some people had not worked for years in the departments where their names appeared. The result—two budgets were incorrect. One did not have enough expense in it. The other had too much allowance.

Usually your first problem is one of rearranging expenses. See that each expense is wholly self-contained, regardless of where amounts were charged previously. Keep in mind that the second key is to fix responsibility for the control of expense.

WHO IS RESPONSIBLE?

In more than one instance, you will have to answer the question, "Who is responsible?" Take the case of a service department. Who is responsible for the control of maintenance costs? You may argue that the supervisors who use maintenance services are the ones responsible. That raises a couple of questions:

Define Responsibility fully

1. Who controls the performances of the maintenance force?

2. Who decides what work is necessary for proper maintenance?

Yes, I know that a foreman who lets his equipment be mistreated should be blamed. To charge him with maintenance costs is one way to do it. But that is like charging him for material costs when all he can control is the excess scrap. My opinion is that we make these charges for cost-accounting reasons. Anyhow, charging or prorating is more apt to lose than to gain control. I would keep together all of one kind of expense. In this example, I would hold the maintenance supervisor responsible. Somewhere up the line is the responsibility for maintaining the proper relation between maintenance costs and production.

START WITH PAYROLLS

You can avoid some of the problems indicated. For one thing, start with payrolls. These show wages and salaries paid. These basic expenses are usually self-contained. They are not affected by cross charges. I start with wages for another reason. Experience shows that wages are the most controllable of the three types of expense.

1. *Wages* are payrolls of every kind.
2. *Charges* are expenses for supplies.
3. *Fixed* expenses are items like depreciation.

You can show that there are a number of payroll costs that are less controllable than some I classify as charges. And, too, there may be transpositions from one to the other. One example is outside contracting for maintenance or toolroom work.

In general, however, there are two differences. One is that charges are somewhat like indirect materials. The other is that charges usually have in them a larger proportion of constant expense. Perhaps you can see this better in Fig. 18.

So if you start with payrolls, you don't have to unscramble a lot of cross prorations. Likewise, if you can get the original amounts for charges and fixed expenses, you can eliminate a great deal of detailed work.

In timestudy, I learned "you can add 'em together, but try to take 'em apart." The same applies here. Do not try to hurry your analysis by grouping accounts. Rather, take them in the smallest subdivisions of original entry. Two reasons seem important enough to mention. First, small amounts can often be relocated in total. Second, individual accounts will probably have quite different trend lines with respect to volume. If you have 150 to 200 accounts, that's fine. You will be glad you have so many small ones later on.

Fig. 18. Simplified charts showing the three types of expenses with relations of constant costs to variable slopes.

WHAT CONTROL CYCLE?

Wages, charges, and fixed expenses may exist in three groups. These we will call manufacturing, selling, and administrative. You will see these cross divisions illustrated in Fig. 19.

Here you may ask, "Why this type of split?" There are two reasons. First, I think that selling and administrative expenses

EXPENSES	WAGES	CHARGES	FIXED
MANUFACTURING			
SELLING			
ADMINISTRATIVE			

Fig. 19. You may have the three types of expense in the three divisions of overhead.

are costs, not deductions from gross profit. But remember that I am an engineer. Second, manufacturing may take place at a greatly different time of the year from selling. For control, we must be able to measure manufacturing expense against production for any given period. In contrast, selling expense should be compared with sales. What administrative should be measured against is anybody's guess. Perhaps the best we can do with administrative is to relate it to the combination.

You may decide that some items formerly carried in sales or administrative should be included in manufacturing costs. The reverse decision may be made. I remember one case where, in effect, manufacturing conversion had in it almost everything but profit. The boss man's explanation was that he wanted to collect all costs in case of fire. I think I convinced him that charging sales expense into inventory did not make it collectible if the plant burned down.

You determine what expenses, if any, are to be switched around. This is done by using two guides:

1. Is the expense a part of inventory?
2. Is the expense proportional to production or sales?

TREND OF EXPENSE

If you are to predict expense for different volumes, you must know their trends. These relations between dollars of expenses and units of volume you can get most easily by plotting curves. For the curves to be representative, you should have three, preferably five to ten, periods of cost experience. The range in volume included is more important than the number of periods. You should have maximum and minimum volume experienced in the current past. I use current advisedly. Many important changes are going on at all times. The figures used should be year's totals. You see, most businesses are affected by seasonal cycles that cause one main peak and one decided valley to come within each year.

You should trace back through several years of past history. How many? That depends upon several factors:

How reliable are your figures?
How many points determine a line?
How wide a spread in volume can you get?

In the best analysis I ever worked with, we used 10 years. Probably 5 years will be satisfactory. However, the range in volume we had in the 10 years was from the depression low to the largest volume ever turned out by the company. From this, I would suggest a range approaching highest to one-third of highest volume.

Right away, you can see how much rearranging you have to do. You must get expenses lined up to conform with your present organization. All the year expenses must be comparable before you plot them. If they are not, as I cited before, you make two errors.

CHECK YOURSELF

To get under way, get some long sheets of multicolumn paper. I don't mean columnar pads. These are cumbersome. They have too much space per column. They have many lines for separately posting dollars and cents. This feature is fine for vertical additions. But you will want to add horizontally. Also, you won't want to be bothered with pennies.

You can line up your expense accounts across the top. Place years vertically. Arrange the accounts in the three subdivisions, Wages, Charges, and Fixed. Set up separate sheets for Manufacturing, Selling, and Administrative. In heading your columns, try to group accounts according to responsibilities but without mixing wages, charges, and fixed. Record all your starting figures, and set up totals by groups.

Now the fun begins. You will see as you glance down certain columns that expenses change greatly. What caused the marked changes? Often these represent shifts in organization structure. You must track down these shifts. Further analysis and shifts of figures are necessary. You want to ensure that the figures you plot for a stated expense represent that responsibility throughout the entire period analyzed.

As you locate organization changes, you rearrange the money. You take from one column and add to another. Check yourself before you go too far. I know from experience that you can lose half a day finding an error. So, after you have made a few transpositions, see that you still come back to your starting totals. Make a few more shifts. Check again. Eventually, you will have all accounts representing the present expense responsibilities. Expenses for all years will be comparable.

WHAT KIND OF DOLLARS?

I said that the rearranged expenses for any one account should be comparable in order to plot them. This is true. But it raises the question of inflation. What kind of dollars are we attempting to compare? At the same time, the value of the dollars is only one question. There are two others:

1. If wages are up 70 per cent, would you necessarily spend 70 per cent more for the work? You might eliminate some because you could not afford it.

2. If there has been any progress in method improvement, you would not expect to spend as much again if you repeated the past cycle.

You can attempt to outguess these interacting influences by adjusting dollars. However, my personal preference is to plot the actuals. Then make your adjustments on the trend lines after the curves are drawn. My chief reason for postponing dollar adjustments is because there are others to be made on the basis of policy.

CHAPTER 8

PLOT EXPENSES FOR TREND LINES

Most of the expenses we talked about in Chap. 7 are called "semivariable" in accounting circles. You may call them what you like. I prefer to avoid such classifying. I don't see how to draw the lines between variable, semivariable, and fixed. As a matter of fact, I won't admit that any expense is fixed. I've seen buildings torn down to change that condition.

At any rate, you have a flock of expense figures to analyze. Your overhead costs, especially those of overhead labor, are not proportional either to direct labor or to sales dollars. We recognize that fact when we admit we have break-even points. These are caused by the substantial "costs to open the door." These costs are chiefly the constant portions of overhead wages and salaries.

SETUP PRORATIONS

Prorating such constants over various quantities causes marked fluctuations in unit costs. That's what is wrong with expense ratios of any kind. You can see why. If $1,000 is the constant expense and 100 units the volume, then the proration is $10 per unit of volume. But the per unit cost is $20 when the volume drops to 50 per cent. Likely variations in the range of volume are reflected in the shifting costs.

Volume Units	Constant Cost	Cost per Unit
150	$1,000	$ 6.67
125	1,000	8.00
100	1,000	10.00
75	1,000	13.33
50	1,000	20.00

Let me emphasize this shifting ratio with graphics. Take a look at Fig. 20. Curve (*a*) represents the common type of expense-volume relation. It shows our constant cost of $1,000 plus a variable cost of $2,000 at 100 per cent volume. To get cost per unit of sales or production, we divide total expense at a given volume by that volume. The results show in curve (*b*), Fig. 20.

CONSTANT AND VARIABLE

To make my point, I want to break down this pair of curves, Fig. 20 (*a*) and (*b*), into its parts. Notice the (*c*) and (*d*) pair. These represent the true variable with volume. I say "true" because the cost per unit is the same at any volume. I think that the supposition of such conditions is one reason why so many people use ratios.

Now look at the other part of our starting curve—the constant. You see in curve (*e*) the constant carried across for all volumes. In (*f*), you see an ordinary reciprocal curve ($1/X$). This shows the unadulterated effect of straight proration. The cost per unit is different, but the curve part itself is the same as that in (*b*). It differs in amount only by the variable cost per unit shown on curve (*d*).

AMOUNT VS. RATE

Our mixed thinking may stem from the words we use. You can see from this breakdown of the usual curve that

A constant element of expense becomes
a variable cost per unit.
A variable element of expense becomes
a constant cost per unit.

Of course, this apparent contradiction is the result of dividing one set of numbers by another. But we need to understand the effect. We must recognize the opposites of amount and rate. We say "variable and semivariable" in speaking of expenses. Here we mean amount. Yet, practically all expense curves have constant amounts in them. Even direct labor does. The constant is introduced because we hold on to the more highly skilled people when we reduce the work force. This raises the average hourly rate.

$$\text{EXPENSE} = \text{CONSTANT} + (\text{Slope})(\text{Vol})$$
$$y = b + Mx$$

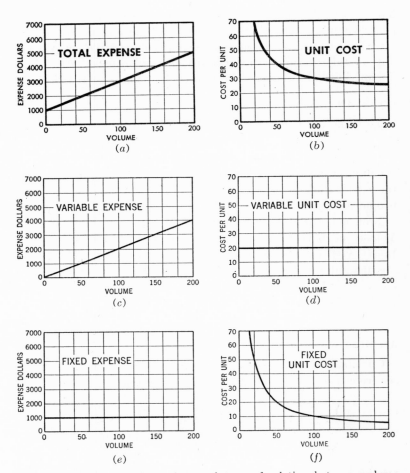

Fig. 20. (*a*) Here we have the usual type of relation between volume
and expense. (*b*) You get a curve like this one when you divide the expenses of curve (*a*) by their corresponding volumes. (*c*) This is the
variable expense only taken from the total shown on curve (*a*). (*d*) Notice
that the "unit cost" of the variable expense in curve (*c*) is the same for
any volume. (*e*) Only the fixed or constant portion of the total expense
curve (*a*) is shown here. (*f*) You can see here that the "unit cost" of the
constant expense in (*e*) varies inversely with volume.

PRODUCTION PLOTTING

I guess it's long experience with timestudy data that makes me think that the only approach to sound expense analysis is through curve plotting. Maybe it is an engineering habit. It is the best I know, anyhow. It brings out constant amounts you'd never suspect. After all, it's the *right answer* we seek, isn't it? So plotting is our next step.

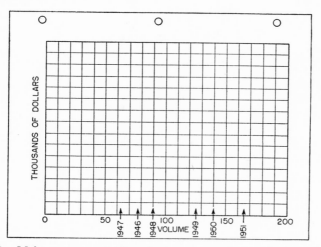

Fig. 21. Make up your plotting sheets on a production basis and mark off your volume scale for specific years. Expect the years to be out of sequence because volume increases and declines over a period of time.

With a probable quantity of 150 to 200 curves, I'd go at the job on a production basis. Set up a supply of 8½ by 11 cross-section sheets with volume across the long side. All sheets can be marked specifically for the volumes and years corresponding with those you are using (see Fig. 21). Then adopt four or five standardized ranges in dollars for your vertical scales. Make up your curve sheets by some duplicating process.

VOLUME MEASURE

What do you use to measure volume, you ask? We talked about that subject at length in Chaps. 4 and 6. You may want to review what was said there. I think it should be standard minutes or *Units* of pure direct labor. Of course, Standard Hours that are equivalent to good pieces are the same thing.

After that come direct labor hours, direct labor dollars, tons, and sales dollars in declining correctness in the order named. You have to do the best you can with what you have. You can't plot curves without some measure of volume. Be sure you recognize the errors I stressed. The several years' volumes you are using have changed with respect to each other. These changes place the true volumes at different locations along the base line.

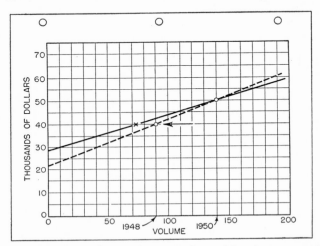

FIG. 22. Your volume changes in comparison with other years with improvements in productivity, as this chart portrays.

As these move one way or the other, the slope of the expense line changes. To show what I mean, Fig. 22 is drawn. Our figures are:

Year	Volume	Expense
1948	90	$40,000
1950	140	50,000

To illustrate the change in volume figures, I have assumed an improvement in productivity of 20 per cent. If 1950 performance is taken as 100, then 1948 is about 83 per cent of the 1950 equivalent. Therefore, its volume of 90 in terms of 1950 is actually only 75 (90 × 100/120). This change moves the volume horizontally to a new location. Notice what that does to the slope of the curve. More especially, take note of the marked increase in the constant cost at zero volume.

CORRECT THE VOLUME

We forget that dollars are not dollars unless we put date stamps on them. So we must get all our figures converted to the same terms. This applies just as emphatically to correct time-study standards, if there have been marked changes. My concern here is with the common types of timestudy "rates" that conceal changes. I can only suggest what to adjust for.

Setups, scrap, rework. Indirect costs to put through orders go up when quantities decline.

Performance. Output per man-hour often rises with decline in volume. The net effect would depend upon whether setups were in or out of the figures.

Wages. Wages have gone up repeatedly. So dollar figures would have to be adjusted for this and the output change.

Tonnage. If I had to use a tonnage measure, I would try to get man-hours along with it. Then I would try to get the man-hours corrected for productivity changes. Next, I would sample each year to see what the man-hours per ton were to find out how much the type of business had shifted.

Sales Dollars. From my point of view, you haven't lived right if you are forced to use sales dollars. They must be corrected for price change, material-content change, all the others you can think of. Then throw them out the window and use your best guess.

When you have corrected your volume measures so that they equal the same productions as your most recent figures, then check one other factor. What is the lag between sales and production? The question is, "Can we logically plot sales expense against the same measure of volume that we use for production expense?"

CURVE PLOTTING

I know I have brought in a lot of ifs, ands, and buts. And there are more to come. Just the same, you don't want to fool yourself.

At this stage, we should have our volumes marked off where they should be. Our expenses should be lined up in each account to agree with today's organization (Chap. 7). Our curves can now be plotted, and they should have some meaning. Each account is plotted on a separate sheet. Of all those you have, only the fixed need not be plotted.

Fixed expenses are more apt to be determined by policy or tax ruling. Whatever they are currently are the amounts to be used. Nevertheless, my inclination would be to draw in these amounts on curves. Then, you will have all expenses represented in your graphs.

DRAWING CURVES

Having plotted your points, you are ready to draw in line relations. The curves you draw must represent the relation between expenses and volumes. Usually, a straight line curve is sufficiently accurate. I would draw these by inspection. Both suggestions are practical ones. Don't lose sight of the fact that probably your expenses were uncontrolled. For that reason, I can't see going to the second decimal place to analyze an expense that is probably 30 per cent excessive.

In drawing your lines, pay special attention to the high- and low-volume points. Control of expenses is likely to be best at these points. At the high point, it often happens that people are scarce. Those you had may have worked diligently to keep up. Maybe you skipped doing less essential things. Offsetting this is the added expense of inefficiency of new people added. What the net effect is, you can guess better than I can.

At the low point, we concentrate on staying solvent. Much tinsel is cut away. Generally, the people working are the more skilled and efficient. These reasons do not apply, however, if the low and high points you use do not represent extremes.

LINES NOT CURVED

You may find some plottings that indicate curved lines. Such curved relations may have been forced by putting on extra heavy pressures during low periods and "taking off the lid" in boom time.

You have to draw a line for an expense even if it does not seem to have any rhyme or reason to it. In such cases,

1. You should thoroughly investigate every point that is far enough out of line to be in error.

2. You must avoid drawing a line that, extended, will cross the volume axis to give a minus constant expense.

3. You want to consider how the expense should be controlled in the future.

You can see that most of the lines will slope uphill. Expense will increase with added volume. Don't be surprised, however, if you find one headed the other way. Advertising is an example. A reverse slope is not illogical. Shouldn't we do more advertising when we need business? Should we raise our advertising budget when we have more business than we can handle?

ADJUSTING CURVES

In trying to figure out where to draw curves, I suggested considering control in the future. That opens up another subject. It has to do with drawing the line "where it should be." [1] And, I think, we should approach our solution in two steps.

To start off, we must remember two very important influences that are hidden in our curves:

1. The points represent "historical expenses." In this I assume that you are setting up controls that did not exist before. Therefore, the expenses were not controlled to the degree you plan for the future.

2. The points include many inconsistencies with respect to current practices. You have attempted to correct for changes in organization responsibilities and process improvements.

Then you have a third consideration. What should the expenses be in the future? This question breaks down into two:

a. What do you propose to spend in the future for a given element of expense?

b. What do you plan with respect to incentives for cost control?

All this is by way of saying, "You are going to budget expenses for the future." That means, you have to think ahead.

---

[1] Carroll, Phil, "How to Chart Timestudy Data," Chap. 9, McGraw-Hill Book Company, Inc., New York, 1950.

You can go at it the way that seems easiest for you. My own preference is to do it in two steps:

1. I would draw in the curves that seemed to show the best relation between expense and volume, then

2. I would locate a second set of curves as required, to depict the probable future trend lines.

To me, it seems much more logical to move a curve than to adjust a number of points. Both curves should show. They are indicated in Fig. 23 (*a*) and (*b*).

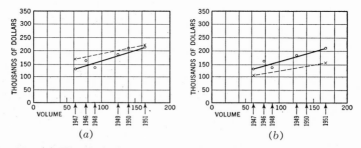

(*a*)   (*b*)

Fɪɢ. 23. (*a*) The dashed curve is an adjustment upward from the curve representing historical expenses. (*b*) Lower your curves from past experience when there are planned improvements in expenses.

Curve (*a*) portrays a dashed line marked by X's that has been set up from the curve of historical expense. The upward movement of the curve could be the result of increases in wage level.

Curve (*b*) exemplifies a reduction. This might be the result of planned method change. It may reflect a proposed change in organization. In this event, the reduction made here should be added to another curve. In contrast, the lowering of the curve could indicate an elimination of expense.

1. You just aren't going to spend that much.
2. You are cutting out the known inefficiencies.
3. You will introduce cost-reduction incentives.

Any way you look at it, you would expect the curves to move in the future. Better control should lower them. Wage increases may raise them if you do not offset the tendency with better methods. The best you can do now is to set up your base lines for measuring progress. You can follow up in at least three ways:

1. Plot current expenses as they occur on the curves you set up.

2. Set up budgets from the curves and show variances.

3. Introduce incentives to get those who spend the money to take a selfish interest in controlling expenses.

CURVE READINGS

When the curves are complete, you want to change them to numbers. This amounts to writing the equations of straight lines. These are simple to prepare. They provide you with a very easy

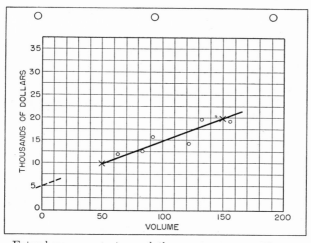

Fig. 24. Extend your curve to read the constant cost. Then take readings at two extremes in volume you can conveniently pick off.

and fast way to set budgets. If you need more dope on this subject, you will find enough in Chap. 11 of "How to Chart Time-study Data." [2]

Most of your curves will be straight lines. Practically all will have some expense for zero volume. This latter is called a *constant* in the equation of a straight line. The rate of change of the variable with production is called the *slope*. Our equation then becomes

$$\text{Expense} = \text{Constant} + \text{Slope} \times \text{Volume}$$

All you need are two figures, constant and slope.

[2] Carroll, *op. cit.*

1. *Constant* is the reading of the curve at zero volume.

2. *Slope* is the rate of increase of expense with expanding volume.

You can read the constants by extending the curves until they cross the dollar-expense scale. If you want these more exact, you will have to go through the equation method. Let's try an example.

In Fig. 24, I have extended a curve until it crosses the dollar axis. The dashed line passes through $5,000, our constant cost. Now for the slope. Let's set down the procedure in steps.

Step 1. Read the curve at the largest volume you can determine correctly. This is $20,000 for 150 volume.

Step 2. Read the curve at the lowest point you can conveniently. Here, we will use $10,000 at 50 volume.

Step 3. Set down these amounts in an orderly arrangement:

Point	Volume	Dollars
1	150	20,000
2	50	10,000

Step 4. Subtracting,   100   10,000
Step 5. Dividing,

$$\frac{\$10{,}000}{100 \text{ Vol}} = \$100/\text{Unit Volume}$$

Step 6. Prove your solution by taking an example different from any used in computing your slope. At a point of 100 volume, the expense should be $100 slope × 100 volume + $5,000 constant.

That works out to be $15,000. The curve reads the same amount, so our zero and slope figures are correct. Now if we place our two factors in our equations, we have

$$\text{Expense} = \$5{,}000 + \$100 \times \text{Volume}$$

In equation form, we portray the mathematical relation between expense and volume. In practice, you simply set up your figures in two columns, properly identified.

Expense	Constant	Slope
Trucking......	$ 5,000	$100
Sweeping......	7,500	30
Checkers......	10,000	173

From such curve factors, you can easily figure your budgets. More on this subject in our next chapter.

CONSTANT COST

Before going on, I think we should stress this expense I have called "constant." You will be surprised at the magnitude of the constant expenses as you get further into this curve plotting. I believe, too, that you will be amazed to find how much of it is not what most people have called "fixed." The fixed portion is relatively small. It may be not over one-fifth of the total constant in your company. Of course, a true curve of expense would probably bend down very sharply as zero volume was approached. But you are not interested in the true curve at low volume. The sheriff would be so close to your door.

Certainly, the constant expense is a very essential derivative of your curve analysis. It is very important in all phases of your control efforts. Unless you know the cost to keep the doors open, you can't very well figure costs for any other volume of business. And this is most important in your control of expenses.

CHAPTER 9

SETTING YOUR EXPENSE BUDGETS

Budgets are estimates made in advance of operations—predictions. Essentially, they must be based on two big "ifs." One is volume of sales or income. If we sell certain products at specified prices, we will have the forecast income. Reasons why you should make sales forecasts, I will mention in Chap. 18. In this chapter, I want to carry on with expense budgeting.

GOOD, BETTER, BEST

Many expense budgets are determined from past performances. Much of the wage and salary expense is still on a daywork basis. Very few budgets carry with them any real incentives to improve performances. You can see then that budgets as gauges of output are comparable with the measurement of shopwork as it was done about 1900. That date is purely arbitrary. It simply illustrates the historical relation between the two gauges of output, timestudy and budget.

You know that we have incentive standards in some plants that are only guesses. In others, there are excellent standards based on sound timestudy. You recognize that there are many grades in between. The same applies to budgets. Budget is a word like standard. It does not have degrees of quality in its meaning. But do not misunderstand. For my money, any budget is better than trusting to the weather, as many companies do.

This comparison with timestudy measurement should emphasize the fact that there is plenty of room for improvement. You should keep in mind what can and has been done by means of good incentive. You should make an even more strenuous effort to obtain a higher degree of reliability in the budget as a measure with its corresponding improvements in costs.

I hasten to say that expense control by means of budgets is a very constructive development. At the same time, you should not forget that budgets lack the dynamo of incentive reward and the stability of measured performance.

PAST PERFORMANCES

For the reasons given, I cannot agree that, "obviously, the best guide to future costs is past costs." [1] Nor do I agree that people should be asked what they think of the amounts that are to be their budgets. This is a little like what Glenn Gardiner calls "the cost of spending." You may agree with G. Charter Harrison. He says, "In many respects a budget is a detriment rather than an aid to profits, in that it puts a business organization into a strait jacket and thereby definitely discourages initiative." [2] On the other hand, you may feel as stated by Metropolitan Life. "From the standpoint of adjustment, the budget places less emphasis on the curtailment of expenditure—which may lead to a penny-wise and pound-foolish policy—than on the wise apportionment of resources in a manner to yield most lasting benefit." [3]

To establish budgets, some folks set up definite expenses for stated volumes. They may choose steps like 80, 90, 100, 110, or 120 per cent of volume. Then they assume or build up probable dollar amounts for each of the items of expense. This procedure creates steps in budget variations that are too wide. Besides, the amounts of money are arbitrarily established according to someone's opinion.

SETTING STAKES

There is some logic in the method if the attempt is made to set goals of better performance. Such budgets ought to produce cost reductions. To the extent that they do, they are an improvement on historical costs. Budgets worked out from historical costs are only a good beginning. If you meet such budgets, you are "holding your own." If you want to make progress, you have to get under your budgets.

[1] Henrici, Stanley B., "Standard Costs for Manufacturing," p. 235, McGraw-Hill Book Company, Inc., New York, 1947.

[2] Harrison, G. Charter, "The Dead Hand of John Gough," p. 11, Madison, Wis., 1941.

[3] "The Budget As an Aid to Management," pp. 1–2, Metropolitan Life Insurance Company, 1940.

Back in 1925, Arch Struthers argued with me about budgets. He maintained that each year his expenses were lowered from the year before. No doubt he was right. His mistake was in saying, "We would have gotten down to your standards in time." Disregarding whatever the losses may have been "in time," he was off base in logic. Most people cannot attain standard when they don't know what it is. They can approach it by trial and error. But they are rarely able to attain it.

Consider budgets from this angle. They are money expressions for work to be done by people paid out of all payroll items. Would you get the same amounts if you approached your solution with a stop watch? Certainly not. I agree that some overhead work is difficult to measure by timestudy. Yet, I know from many experiences that timestudy standards rarely come out the same as "guesstimated" "rates." And budgets, in the usual sense, are so far from incentive "rates" that there is but slight comparison.

STOP OR CONTROL

Ordinary budgets are but a short cut, like group incentives and profit sharing. They do not specify either the work to be done or the number of times it is to be done. What happens with budgetary control, in many instances, is that the work is postponed or abandoned when the budget runs out.

I worked in a plant that controlled maintenance costs just that way. For each job, a work order was set up with a time estimate. As work was done, time was charged. Those charges were subtracted from the remainder. When the estimated time ran out, the work stopped. The estimate could have been wrong. The work may have been done inefficiently because there were no incentives. This was not your plant, so maybe some time was charged to "jobs that could carry it."

Budgets may hold the time or dollar amounts to some predetermined level. But what assurance have you that the work was done? If it can be abandoned, why not eliminate such work entirely? Why, in effect, reduce spending only because you don't have the money? That is not cost control. That is not the way you set up your shop operations. You cannot stop work on a customer's order simply because the price you quoted runs out.

More on this subject in Chap. 23 when we go into indirect incentives.

PREDICTING EXPENSES

What our overhead expenses should be we don't know. Stanley B. Henrici says, "A budget cost is . . . in no sense a standard." [4] But you can gain control and begin to improve costs by budgeting. Budgets have definite advantages in controlling expenses *before* they are spent. If control is exercised, the actual expenses should conform. Such results are fairly easy to achieve when operations are kept at the same level. The real values of budgeting show when there are major changes in volume. It is under these conditions that your predictions can be used to prepare for expansion or contraction.

To gain this advantage, you should prepare budgets before the beginning of the period. With these, you can guide management before and during that period. Action can be taken to overcome variances before it is too late. Also, you can gauge the degree of control exercised by the individuals held accountable.

MONTHLY AMOUNTS

The curves of expenses we worked out in Chap. 8 make a good basis for expense budgets. They furnish us with the basic figures. We know the constant costs at zero volume and the variable costs per unit of volume.

Of course, if you used yearly figures to plot your curves, the constants and variable expenses are annual amounts. To change these to monthly amounts, you should try to use 4- and 5-week months. Too bad we don't have the 13-month calendar.

Four weeks—you divide by 13.0

Five weeks—you divide by 10.4

These figures disregard holidays and vacations. You will want to make adjustments for whatever shutdowns you have. And, since you have to record your working data some place, why not do so in a convenient form? I would list constants and slopes by groups of accountability. Then they are in shape for budget

[4] Henrici, *op. cit.*, pp. 28–29.

| | Constant | | Slope per 1,000 Units |
	4-Week	5-Week	
Direct.................	$16,935	$20,542	$25.152
Direct.................	$16,935	$20,542	$25.152
Supervision..............	$ 2,941	$ 3,566	$ .283
Engineering.............	2,374	2,881	.715
Trucks.................	2,203	2,673	.981
Power House............	1,437	1,743	.151
General...............	$ 8,955	$10,863	$ 2.130
Maintenance.............	$ 2,693	$ 3,268	$ 1.883
Jigs and Fixtures........	231	280	3.452
Patterns...............	327	397	.416
Maintenance..........	$ 3,251	$ 3,945	$ 5.751
Managers...............	$ 4,036	$ 4,894	$ .199
Purchasing..............	841	1,021	.334
Storekeeping............	8,033	9,740	.914
Production Control......	3,392	4,114	.998
Timestudy..............	2,725	3,306	.913
Accounting.............	5,466	6,632	.316
Personnel..............	1,144	1,388	.117
Laboratory.............	1,010	1,225	.103
Guards................	3,062	3,714	.127
Staff.................	$29,709	$36,034	$ 4.021
Total Payroll........	$58,850	$71,384	$37.054

Fig. 25.   Payroll budget figures set up for groups of responsibilities. The slopes per unit of volume are the same, but the constant amounts are computed for 4- and 5-week months.

making. Figure 25 is an example. Note that these figures are groupings of curve readings for payroll expenses only.

SETUP PLUS OPERATION

These two sets of costs, constants and slopes, are like setup and operation standards in wage-incentive computations. The total time for an order equals the setup standard plus so many pieces multiplied by the operation standards. We can figure out before the order is run what the total standard time should be. This is a necessary step in good production planning. In the same way, a budget amount is equal to

Constant + Slope × Volume

All you need to "guesstimate" is the volume. Then you can make up budgets in whatever detail you feel you need.

BUILDING BUDGETS

From constant and slope amounts like those shown in Fig. 25 you can set up your budgets for any volume forecast. You simply multiply each slope by volume and add its constant. Figure your budgets in advance by using volume in round numbers. You can prepare tables for the purpose of establishing forecast budgets in "round" figures. In such tables, I suggest you use increments of volume of about 5 per cent. That will hold your probable differences to 2½ per cent.

At the close of each period, you should correct your budget amounts to correspond with your actual volume. You do this by multiplying your actual volume by the variable expenses per unit of volume and adding the constant expenses. The resulting amounts are then compared with your actual expenses. The differences are called variances. Some are gains—savings. They're OK. We'd like to have them all that way. The others are losses. Here's where control begins. What you folks do to correct these excesses will determine the usefulness of budgets in your cost control. I will say more about variances in Chap. 14. Let me ask here if you think all this seems like a lot of work. Well, it isn't. You will find that a good comptometer operator can compute budgets for 150 accounts in about one hour.

And if you want to get more details on budgeting, I suggest

you read Fred Gardner's "Variable Budget Control." [5]   Also, Edmund LaRose has written many excellent papers on this subject for NACA publications.

FITTING THE ORGANIZATION

To get the results you want, your budgets must do two things for you. First, they must fit current conditions. That does not mean you should allow actual expenses shown in your analysis of past history. Rather, you should think of those actuals as uncontrolled amounts to progress from.

Second, your budgets must be lined up according to accountability for the control of expenses. Then, you should compare budgets with actuals to measure the degree of control exercised by those individuals responsible. Otherwise, how can you tell who is doing a good job? How can you find out who can be given the bigger job to handle?

When you get these two fundamentals clicking, you should

1. Expect progress in cost reduction.
2. Detect weakness in personnel.
3. Correct judgments in predictions.

These advantages are important in any progressive business. Remember, however, that budgets you set up as I suggest here are only rough yardsticks. All your past costs covered mixed products. Later, you will want to find out how these expenses should shift with changes in product mix. Even so, you are starting an important cost control when you set up any expense budgets.

[5] Gardner, Fred V., "Variable Budget Control," McGraw-Hill Book Company, Inc., New York, 1940.

CHAPTER 10

WHAT ABOUT MATERIAL COSTS?

Actual costs vary all over the lot unless you control them. The amount of variation depends upon (1) how much control you exert and (2) what you use as your gauge. Naturally, if your allowances are liberal, you aren't pushed too hard to stay within limits.

Your manufacturing and selling costs may be the big elements in your control problem. They are in most companies where I have worked. For that reason, I'm directing practically all this book to the control of conversion costs. But we do use materials. They do cost plenty. And to the extent that their costs are controllable, we must go to work on them. This stage seemed as good as any to inject the subject of material costs.

MATERIAL STANDARDS

Variations in material costs are sometimes greater than all the others combined. My experience is that our variations occur largely because we have little control. Control is lacking, I think, because we have not set up guideposts. This suggests the need for standardization. By using standard material costs, you can gain several desirable results:

1. Consistency in costing.
2. Convenience in cost and price revisions.
3. Ease in inventory revaluing.
4. Measures of variations in price level.
5. Measures of usage variations.

Standard material costs or prices may be set up by your Purchasing Department. They should select prices that are considered to be normal. These actual prices are relatively unimportant in themselves. They are only figures picked out of a hat. As you can see, any prices within reason will serve as base lines for measuring variances.

PRICE-CHANGE INDEX

Variances are only indicators, to my way of thinking. They should not become the "tail that wags the dog." So they must be kept within reason. And the limits are, theoretically, those that are within the control of the organization. Of course, that alone gives us plenty of room for argument.

If you put the "heat" on Mr. Purchaser, he will say, "I can't do anything about prices." Mr. Salesman will say, "I have to conform to my customer's wishes. I can't tell you in advance. How can anyone read the customer's mind?" And so it goes.

Regardless, you need guideposts. Your material "cost-of-living index" should be reported periodically by Purchasing. And when the index shows a tendency to exceed some limits you have set, then costs and prices may need to be revised.

You can approach this limit-setting in a practical way. Suppose that material cost is 40 per cent of your total. Then, if material costs increase 25 per cent, your over-all change is 10 per cent.

	Standard		Current
Material Cost.........	40	$+25\%$	50
Conversion Cost.......	60		60
	100		110

Ten per cent change over all may be too much for your business. But this indicates a way to set limits to minimize the

Refiguring of detailed costs.
Shifting of base-line comparisons.
Revising of price schedules.

On the other hand, there is an offsetting disadvantage you must watch. If you are thinking of control as distinguished from accounting, you must continually pound down the plus variances. Yet, you know as well as I do that you can't blame someone for an excess cost that is beyond his control. So you have to straddle, unless you go to more refinement. You have to recognize some variance as not controlled as you gain the advantage of wider index limits.

EXTRAS INCLUDED

Standard order quantities should be established for each product in order to determine suitable quantity extras. You set extras for all other factors, such as specification, size, tolerance, and freight, for each class of items to add to the base price. This total becomes the standard material price for each purchased item.

To maintain your inventory at standard, you price every invoice for purchased material at the established standard price for that material. The difference between standard and actual cost on each invoice is a variance. The proper proportion of the month's total may be taken into your current month's operating profit or loss as a material variance.

Your monthly material variances serve a very important purpose. When any material variance is divided by the total of that material purchased during the month priced at standards, the resulting per cent gives you a measure of the change in level of your purchases. When a variance goes beyond your limits, your standard material costs and selling prices may have to be changed accordingly.

PRICE GROUPS

Sometimes you can group materials into classes or types. For each of these, you can establish one price. This price grouping has a number of advantages. The obvious one is the reduced time to price material invoices.

Another is a smaller number of price indexes to be maintained and reported. But the one I like best is the advantage gained if you happen to make assemblies. Usually, these are made up of several types of material. Their prices may change in different amounts—even in opposite directions. To be able to change the costs of these several materials with ease is a cute trick.

Imagine an assembly made up of steel, aluminum, and brass. Suppose there are a dozen parts in all. In this case, your standard cost cards could have three columns for material. They would be labeled ST, AL, BR. As you price the material for a steel part, you enter its cost in the column headed ST for steel. Similarly, you show the material costs in the proper columns for each part. When all are priced, you add vertically to get separately all the steel, aluminum, and brass used in that assembly. Then you can revise costs for inventory or pricing purposes in totals.

MATERIAL-COST CONTROL

In the main, the control of material cost rests with engineering. Those who design the product usually specify what is to be used. I want to make that point clear. Many people are confused in this phase of control. For example, we must understand that a shop foreman cannot control material costs. All he can work on is the prevention of scrap and waste. Likewise, he cannot reduce the expense of drills, taps, and reamers except as he can cut down on spoilage.

In this, we have a parallel with optional items of overhead expense like route cards, perpetual inventory, or window washing. If we eliminate the ⅝-inch holes, then the foreman does not have to use ⅝-inch drills. If we eliminate one coat of paint, then management, not the foreman, will save some paint.

So I think of material control in three distinct divisions:

1. Engineers can control the basic costs.
2. Shop supervisors can control what I may call usage.
3. Purchasing department can control the prices paid.

And within my limited experience, I think there is a "gold mine" to be uncovered in a study of engineering specifications.

All you can do as a starter is to establish material-cost standards based on specifications as they are. For indirect materials, similar specifications can be established per unit of type, as with drills and grinding wheels, or per unit of output, as with some items like packing supplies.

STANDARD QUANTITY

You need to take another step to standardize quantity. How much material do you need to make a salable article? Ordinarily, you start with the engineering specifications.

But drawings show only the finished piece. Is it punched out of a strip? Is it cut off a bar? First, you allow the necessary waste in fabrication. Then, include a normal scrap loss. Here, you want to be careful.

Historical figures are very treacherous. What you have done for 20 years is not a safe basis to work from. This is especially true if you are starting to set up controls from historical costs recorded during "precontrol" periods. You want to base your standards on what you should do.

Again for consistency, you should standardize. What is reasonable scrap? You should analyze by type of product and by size of lot. Some types are much more hazardous to make. Your investigation should uncover some costly errors in design. Maybe, it's an external problem. Some customers may be too critical for the price they pay.

Also, size of lot has a big influence. Your scrap percentage goes up as your runs become smaller. You might call it the "cost to learn how to make the stuff." Anyhow, line up some standards for scrap-cost inclusions. What if they are tentative? You begin to make progress as soon as you set a base line.

QUANTITY TOLERANCE

One phase of material control I came upon by accident. My exposure occurred about 25 years ago in a plant making lead-covered cable. The thickness of the lead had to be within tolerance, of course. The critical tolerance was minimum thickness because the lead covering was put on to protect the cable.

My job was to help cut costs. Naturally, when I saw lead covering being "stripped" off, I became upset. So I went to the Boss and pounded on the desk. I shrieked, "Two men worked all day yesterday stripping." "Yes, I know," he said calmly. "Let me worry about that rework. If I don't keep two men busy removing 'thin lead,' we're giving away too much material at 6 cents a pound."

Holding tolerance is an important part of cost control. However, oftentimes it is cheaper to give away extra material rather than risk going under the tolerance. I got off base in another case by saying, "Isn't it cheaper to give 'em a little extra than to do all that weighing?" "Oh, no," was the reply, "Uncle Sam wouldn't like it. We might go to jail." You see, here the tobacco tax was involved. But there are very few cases where your customers would complain about a "baker's dozen." Consequently, another source of cost reduction is in the closer adherence to standard size or quality. But don't press too hard for material-cost control when to hold limits will cost you more in other expenses. Here, you have to choose between disadvantages.

CHAPTER 11

YOU SHOULD SET A NORMAL VOLUME

Expenses vary with production only in part. You have a large element of expense I have been calling the "cost of the nucleus of the organization." It is constant, regardless of volume. This includes the costs I have called "fixed." These constant costs are a large percentage of your total expense. In one company, they amounted to over 16 per cent of the total cost of normal sales. In another, they were 23 per cent.

Spreading these constant costs over changing volumes is what causes some of the wild fluctuations in actual product costs. This variation is due to simple arithmetic, as I tried to show in Chap. 3. I think it a mistake for you to clutter up your cost figures with varying prorations of this large constant. Such bookkeeping arithmetic destroys your base line of comparison for cost controls.

NORMAL FORECAST

To stabilize costs, you should make an equitable distribution of this constant expense. You can do this by establishing a volume of business that can be called normal for your company. The definition of Normal Volume I use is "the volume necessary to produce a cost that is fair to your customers and fair to your company."

Your Normal Volume is fairly easy to establish if you have been in the habit of forecasting sales. If you have not, I think you should begin. I will outline reasons why in Chap. 18. Either way, you should set up a Normal Volume.

You can see in advance that a lot of discussion in your executive group will take place before one volume is agreed upon. Usually, this is an amount in dollars. It represents your management's best judgment of a typical year in its widely varying experiences. It may even be selected as the sales for a certain year.

Considering inflation, you know that it is wrong to think of one volume in dollars. Yet, you may find it almost impossible to get your top management to think in any other terms.

But don't worry. Within limits, the dollar amount can be reasonably correct at the moment. It should be one amount because your manufacturing capacity is relatively fixed at the time. And you can check the initial forecast in three ways.

FAIR RETURN

First, you can say that your Normal Volume is "the volume necessary to return a fair profit on your invested capital." Such an approach must consider two important factors:

1. Peaks and valleys over the long-range business operations on both sides of the break-even point.

2. Capital requirements from outside investors or through plowing back earnings.

People who save money demand, and rightly so, a fair return on their investments. They will not buy stocks or bonds that will not produce satisfactory earnings. As we have seen, more and more earnings are being plowed back because there are fewer takers of capital-raising issues. Plowing back reduces the dividends paid. Again, we discourage investors.

Risk is a factor also. We must think of long-range risk. In the short term, you can show that there are plenty of gamblers in stock markets. I'm an engineer, not a financier. I cannot pretend to know what is a fair return. I do feel, however, that it should not be related to "the average of your industry." Your industry competes with all others for "people's savings."

Fifty-three per cent of the people questioned in the *Factory* survey in 1947 thought a profit between 0 and 14 per cent was reasonable.[1] Many of those who expressed opinions were probably not qualified to risk losing their savings.

You can get more slants on profit per cent in "Managing for Profit."[2] On page 37, you will find that profit should be two or three times the going rate of interest. This suggested 12 to 18 per cent in 1937. If you just picked 4 per cent out of a hat

---

[1] *Factory Management and Maintenance,* December, 1947.

[2] Knoeppel, C. E., and E. G. Seybold, "Managing for Profit," McGraw-Hill Book Company, Inc., New York, 1937.

as a "going rate," then 10 per cent would be two and a half times. I suggest you use a straight per cent check, after you "guesstimate" your risks and your volume swings in relation to some known yardsticks like A.T.&T. or U.S. Steel (Fig. 26).

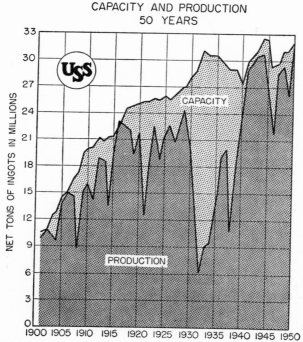

CAPACITY AND PRODUCTION
50 YEARS

Fig. 26. Check your normal volume relation with some standard indicator like U.S. Steel.

NORMAL PIECES

When you have determined your normal volume, your next step is to translate it into pieces. The shop works on pieces, not dollars. Your problem is simplified if some year has been taken as your normal. Your pieces are practically all set for you. But be sure to check carefully the proportions of any one product to the total and to past history. Naturally, you will modify past proportions to suit the likely future volume for each product. Figure 27 shows how proportions of three major lines may shift around in your long-range outlook.

With quantities set, you should ask executives in the sales group to determine normal selling prices for these products. Extending these will give you a second check on the dollar volume assumed. This procedure is an important one. From it, you can

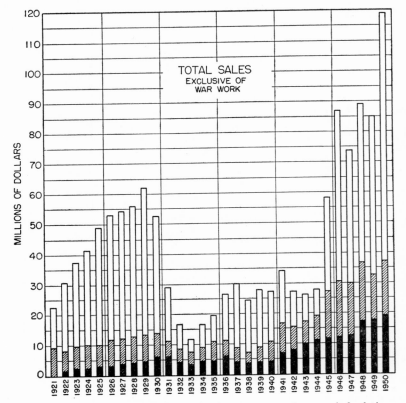

Fig. 27. Notice how the product mix changes over a long period of time.

get the normal selling prices of conversion. These can be used as control figures later on.

NORMAL WORK LOAD

From normal quantities, you get the standard-time work load. In straight manufacturing, this is simply pieces multiplied by standard operation times. I use Units—standard minutes. If you do not use standard-time work measures, you should remember the distortions we discussed in Chap. 4. I will continue with my term Units just so we stay on the same track.

To get work load, you extend by Unit Standards all products you will make in the normal forecast. You do this by operations. You carefully note vertically on big sheets all specific equipment tied in with your operations. Where several machines of a kind are in one group in the same department, you can treat these as a unit. You may take some latitude in this grouping. Where slightly different machines have about the same costs and are used interchangeably, you may treat them as a group.

MACHINE LOAD

Then comes the long, tedious job. You must extend each part of normal quantity by each of its operation standards. These

MACHINE	UNITS	MOTORS	PUMP	GENERAT.	TRANSF.	COMPRES.	DEPREC.
DRILL	102083	4.00 / 3290	63.00 / 53438	30.00 / 25462	1.00 / 1272	22.00 / 18621	120.00
W&S 2a	48752	29.00 / 8643	41.00 / 12431	35.00 / 10640	5.00 / 1632	52.00 / 15406	162.00
BULLARD	34775	180.00 / 10432	147.00 / 8506	111.00 / 6431	— —	162.00 / 9406	600.00
CINN MILL	35470	71.00 / 6932	49.00 / 4763	115.00 / 14407	89.00 / 8663	38.00 / 3705	362.00
		284.00	300.00	291.00	95.00	274.00	1244.00
	221080	29297	79138	53940	11567	47138	

Fig. 28. Use a two-way chart form to collect by products the standard-time work load for Normal Volume. Use two lines per machine or work station to provide for the next step. See Figs. 32, 33, and 34.

results are set down by machines in the departments where the work is done. Big sheets like the section shown on Fig. 28 provide the means for collecting your machine work loads into product groups. Notice the double spacing on this sheet. Later, when the money charges for each machine are set, you can spread these crosswise against your work loads and add vertically by processes.

You may have many more product groups than indicated on my small sample. Also you may use quantities of sheets. Again, I would set up my sheets on a production basis.

DEPARTMENT LOAD

One need for a quantity of sheets comes when you prorate each of the machine charges just mentioned. Another is to break up long lists of machines. I would split up this machine list by departments. In this way, you can get the work load for each section of your plant. Here you get your third check on your Normal prediction. You compare Normal Volume with equipment capacity. My experience in jobbing operations suggests that your normal work load may approximate 65 per cent of your ideal equipment capacity.

SPARE PARTS AND SPECIALS

If you have spare parts or service business of consequence, you must include the probable amounts at normal. This may be done by analyzing all sales of this type for a typical period. Be careful of any conclusions reached from dollar comparisons. You know that the profit margins are often quite different. If your spare parts are included with the stock of regular parts, be sure you get the right proportions of each.

Raise or lower the volume of spare parts to conform with your Normal Volume of new business. This is suggested if you do not take the correct approach by building up a normal forecast of spare parts.

For special products, you should set time standards representative of the sizes and types included in your normal forecast. You may do this by modifying standards for regular work for specials lying in between the typicals. If you follow this method, it is very necessary to include a fair proportion of both of the extreme types. Be sure to include some easy ones and some complex jobs. Standards are extended by forecast quantities and accumulated by work stations by departments for both spare parts and specials. And for the time being, I would keep these separated from the Units of new work. They may have entirely different conversion costs.

DESIGN AND METHOD CHANGES

A note of caution. Keep all your work-load information in details. Retain flexibility so you can revise it with new conditions that will arise in the future. Major changes in design will affect your work standards. Such changes must be checked for their effects on conversion cost of products in the same group. Therefore, it is important that your product group breakdown provide reasonable flexibility. You don't want a change in one of the elements to cause you to disturb your entire cost analysis.

In the same way, major changes in methods will alter conversion costs. In such cases, watch out for a doubling effect. Method improvements alter the work standards. Thus, your measured-time denominator is reduced. This raises the conversion cost. If, also, you spent important sums of money to make the changes, you have increased your expenses. Such changes may be important enough to call for revisions in product costs and budgets. You should stay abreast of these changes. Your yardsticks of control should measure what they are supposed to.

CAPACITY UTILIZATION

Your forecast work load will utilize widely differing percentages of your equipment. Some machine may be used more than 100 per cent of a 40-hour week. Others may work only 10 per cent of the time. Perhaps some of the tools you use infrequently were purchased years ago to extend your manufacturing capacity. Extreme percentages of use are due to unbalanced conditions. Knowing where your unbalances are is useful by-product information you should reveal.

You can compare your normal work load with capacity in any desired detail. Take departments, as one form. What capacity do you have in each department? You can use 100 per cent or a more realistic figure. I prefer to figure ideal capacity in two steps. First, I plan to man all available productive equipment at a 75-Unit Hour or 125 per cent performance. If your departments are not on incentive, you might use some lower figure. This gives gross capacity to turn out standard minutes of work. From this, I deduct losses to production caused by setups and similar indirect labor. The remainder is a practical capacity to turn out salable work.

Then you might set these up in a bar chart like Fig. 29. The heights of the bars indicate the departmental capacities. The cross-hatched portions represent work loads at normal volume.

When you compare these two, you will be amazed. Some departments will be well loaded. Others seem bare. These variations are caused by three factors:

1. Forecast demand is different from the capacity you have.
2. Design and method changes have altered tool load.
3. Machine-tool builders won't sell you half a drill press.

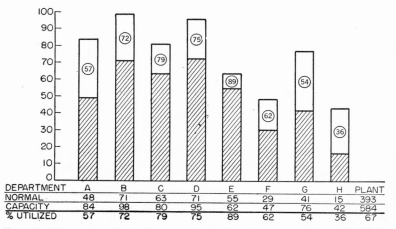

DEPARTMENT	A	B	C	D	E	F	G	H	PLANT
NORMAL	48	71	63	71	55	29	41	15	393
CAPACITY	84	98	80	95	62	47	76	42	584
% UTILIZED	57	72	79	75	89	62	54	36	67

Fig. 29. Show the unbalanced capacity utilization in your Normal Forecast by comparing the projected work against your capacity to produce.

It is impractical to balance facilities, if yours is a job shop. Yet the excess capacity costs you money. For that reason, you should try to relieve the condition in two ways. One is to dispose of unused equipment. The other, more profitable, way is to find products you can make with the excess machine-hours.

You counter with, "Why not run the bottleneck operations on the second shift and balance the equipment that way?" You can, and you do. But note, you have changed your capacity. Per cent of unbalance is the same if you figure both work load and capacity on 80 hours instead of 40. That is the cheaper way to approach the balancing. The other way is to buy more of the bottleneck equipment. Then also you have expanded your capacity. Theoretically, you should increase your Normal Volume.

Remember, you pay and pay when you have peaks and valleys in your operations. To attempt to beat this, you should look for something you can make in spare time or with spare capacity. See if you can find staple articles you can put on the shelf. You can use them to smooth out seasonal changes in work load.

UNUSED CAPACITY

"Suppose we can't use this unbalanced capacity. What then?" you ask. One auditor I know figured everything on the basis of 80 per cent utilization. That is a nice theory. But if 80 per cent is right for some department or machine, it is wrong for many others. The variable of setup alone throws out any one percentage.

Maybe you think it should be carried as "idle capacity." However you figure it, profit winds up the same amount. Uncle Sam writes the rules. Therefore, what you do in figuring is only for internal control. Take note, however, of two things. First, you have idle capacity because normal volume is not maximum. Second, you have some unused capacity because you equipped to meet unusual customer requirements. Both of these belong in cost, as I reason. If my conclusion is correct, then all you could properly show as "idle capacity" would be the leftover resulting from shifts caused by

1. Changes in the character of the business.
2. Design and methods improvements.

Before you get all tangled up in idle-equipment theory, let me make a point. I consider this one to have an important effect on costs that most of us pass by. Let me illustrate with a story.

Bill Moyer, an old friend of mine, was Chief Industrial Engineer of a steel company. He once said, "Phil, you won't believe it but the overhead in one of our mills is $960 an hour." Think of that. Such overhead costs would scare some executives I have known. And to make this even more impressive, let me show you a bit of arithmetic. As you know, steel mills operate 24 hours a day, 7 days a week. That equals 168 hours of productivity per week. Look what would happen to $960 per hour if steel mills operated 40 hours like most plants do.

$$\$960 \times \frac{168}{40} = \$4,032 \text{ per hour}$$

"You couldn't afford to ride in an automobile if steel mills worked only 40 hours." That's what I tell timestudy men in an attempt to make clear the relation between production and cost.

"Who wants to work nights?" you ask. You may add, "You can't shut down a steel mill at suppertime." But what about railroads, telephones, and night clubs? Suppose those were turned off at the end of 8 hours. You couldn't get any place, or call anybody, or even relax.

Don't misunderstand. I'm not arguing for round-the-clock operations. But I am reminded of that old-timer. A rooster happened to go under the fence and found himself in an ostrich farm. Lo and behold, there was an egg half as big as he was. So he returned and brought his hens to see the enormous eggs. Then he said, "Now ladies, I don't wish to criticize. I just want to show you what other folks are doin'."

CHAPTER 12

HOW TO DETERMINE CONVERSION COSTS

What do you think of when you hear the term "marginal mine"? "Their costs are too high." But what costs are you thinking about—ore or process? You reply, "The mine has to spend too much to get out a definite grade ore. There is no profit except when the price is high." Now you are thinking of conversion cost.

Take a very simple example. When you get a flat tire, you take it to the gas station. Someone there makes it round on all sides and charges you the regular price. That price is for fixing the leak. It is the same whether your tire costs $20 or $50.

At one time in World War II, I worked with a company making antiaircraft guns. The plant, the equipment, and the material belonged to the Canadian government. The company operated and managed only. Its costs were those of turning out the product. Its function was solely that of converting.

An example less extreme came up in another plant. The usual product was made of steel. But Andrew Mellon preferred aluminum. The cost of his favorite metal was then seven times that of steel, as I remember it. Assume that the work was the same with either material. Is the overhead cost of the aluminum product seven times that of the steel?

"Wait a minute," you say. "We apply overhead on labor only." My question then is, "How do you treat general overhead?" If you do what most folks do, you add it to material as well as to labor cost. What would you do if your material were gold? Two companies I have worked with made products of precious metals. One added diamonds. What do you think their prices would look like if overheads were added to their material costs?

You can see how large the errors could be in such extremes. Yet many companies make the same basic mistakes in lesser de-

117

grees. My guess is that we do so because we think in dollars instead of work and skills added. I am repeating the ideas expressed in Chap. 5 to set the stage.

WORK ADDED

What we are willing to pay for the article determines how much money the converter has to work with. If what we offer does not cover costs, he will go broke. Basically, that is true. Actually, it may be concealed for several reasons:

1. He may make up his loss on some other products.
2. He may get busy and reduce costs.
3. He may borrow money to tide him over.

Eventually, he may go broke anyway because competition may take our business away from him. We will buy where we can get higher quality, better service, lower price, or perhaps more courtesy. Our efforts here are pointed at items 1 and 2 in that order. You have to know what costs are to work soundly on cost reduction. I state the cost-control problem that way because

1. You can't work on everything at once—so you should be selective.
2. You can effect more improvement, as a rule, by working on the big leaks.
3. You should measure your results in order to control the direction of your efforts.

My approach is opposite that stated by one author.[1] He says the total net "is all that counts for the progress" of the concern, and that allocations of expenses "to show a profit here and a loss there" are "purely imaginary."

OVERHEAD BREAKDOWN

Maybe the difference in viewpoint hinges on the word "allocation." NACA Research [2] thinks you should remember that the *whole is the sum of its parts.* In brief, their report says

1. You have fairly good figures on manufacturing but not on nonmanufacturing costs.

[1] Conant, W. H., "Outworn Business Idols," Barrons, Boston, 1950.
[2] Assignment of Non-Manufacturing Costs for Managerial Decisions, NACA Bulletin, Research Series 18, May, 1951.

2. You use percentage of sales dollars for distributing, marketing, and administrative expenses, thus obscuring "the very differences" you need to know.

3. You know that "some products, territories, and customers are more profitable than others" and that small orders, product variety, and special services "may have an adverse effect on profits."

Before we go on, I want to clear up two points. First, I will try to show that actually we know only little more about manufacturing than nonmanufacturing overheads. Second, that we lose money on small orders, product variety, and special services because we don't know what to charge. In contradiction, I am in favor of "special services." Why not give the customer what he wants? My limited experience indicates that sales costs are lower on "special services." What we need to find out is how much higher are the manufacturing costs.

"Special services" are only a part of your whole problem. Certain of your products may be just as far out of line. Let me repeat that marketing and administrative expenses are but a part of your problem also. You cannot get the right answers until you treat these as costs. Why is selling any less of a cost than engineering, supervision, clerical, maintenance, or timestudy? It isn't. And it must be measured and controlled as a cost if we want cost control, as I interpret it.

WHY COSTS CHANGE

When we use the term "costs," most of us think of part costs or assembly costs. Costs are effects, not causes. The causes are rate multipliers. They are the rates—wages, overheads, material prices. If the rates go up, the costs will go up. If they are brought down, our costs will decline. So I maintain that our control of costs lies in the control of the rates—conversion costs I call them. If we reduce our conversion costs 20 per cent, then the conversion portion of part costs will decrease by 20 per cent. For that reason, we should work on the causes. We should design our cost-control plan to point up the variations from standard conversion costs. Besides, it is possible to get control by this approach. You can't do it through the myriads of part costs.

TWO COST FACTORS

Any conversion cost is the result of two factors—expense and volume. The expense may be high and the volume low, or vice versa. The resulting cost rate is the quotient of

$$\frac{\text{Expense}}{\text{Volume}} = \text{Conversion Cost}$$

With multiple products, we would expect to get multiple rates or conversion costs. Remember, the expense may be high or low because of the type of product, and the method of conversion.

1. Some products are very much more expensive to make than others.

2. Some types of distribution are more costly than others.

3. Some methods of manufacturing and selling are more high-priced than others for getting the same results.

Remember too, the volume may be high or low depending upon the demand for the product and the method of conversion.

1. Our volume of one product may be greater or smaller than our competitors or than other products in our business.

2. Our volume of one product in dollars, hours, or units of productive labor may be greater or smaller relatively according to the methods we use in manufacture.

You can see from this general breakdown that your conversion costs for any one product can be almost any figure.

PRODUCT VS. PROCESS

Products are what we think of when we visualize the output of our plant. Product is the term I have been using to call attention to the cost complexity of the usual enterprise. Now, we have to reach an understanding. We must make the distinction between product and process.

Product is what we place on the shelf or in the hands of our customer.

Process is the path, method, or procedure we use to make and sell the product.

In many cases, we make no mistake if we use these terms interchangeably. Yet we must recognize that it is the method or procedure that creates the cost. Take an example.

Suppose we have one product in two or more general applications. Let's say that one is standard and that others are special. We can ship from stock when the orders are for our standard product. But when our customers order specials, we have to process them through engineering, purchasing, planning, and timestudy. Up goes the cost, although the products are the same, shall we say, to all outward appearances. Does this make clear the difference between product and process? If so, we can move on to the next stage.

HOW MANY PROCESSES?

How many different processes you will have is a question we cannot answer right off. You have to evolve your answer. You get it in three ways—analysis, arithmetic, and interest.

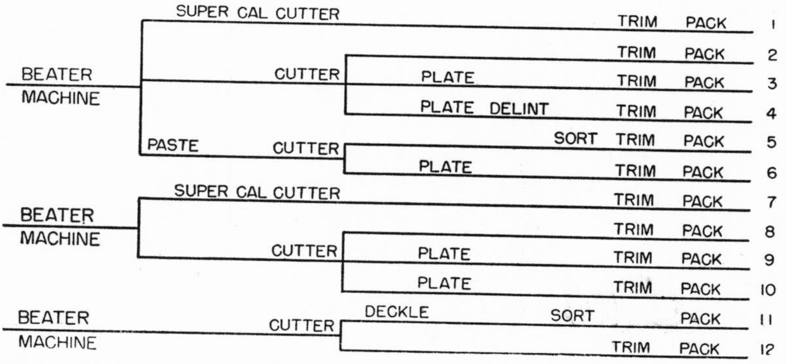

FIG. 30. Line diagrams will assist you in determining what are your several processes.

You start with analysis. You should go at it as I recommend for approaching timestudy standard data. I say, "Plot every suspected difference in an identifying symbol or color." [3] Applying this to cost analysis, you designate each of the suspected different processes you have. One aid is a diagram of your processes (see Fig. 30).

[3] Carroll, Phil, "How to Chart Timestudy Data," p. 117, McGraw-Hill Book Company, Inc., New York, 1950.

Be sure to analyze all the way through. To emphasize, I recall that one plant had to use two process groups for one product. The product was identical in every respect through manufacturing. The difference was in marketing. It was sold to jobbers and to consumers. Jobbing sales expense was over three times that of consumer selling cost.

Using many process groups to start with saves backtracking. Forget about the clerical upkeep. We aren't done yet. Later, we will combine some groups based on the *arithmetic*. And you may not combine certain ones with groupings they could fall into because of your *interest* in watching them individually.

COLLECT ACTIVITY

For your tentative process groupings, you have a check. Any process is a sequence. Thus the relation of any one operation to its total should be fairly constant. Otherwise, you have combined processes. At the same time, if the percentage of any one is low, its effect on the total process cost is negligible. Suppose you have one operation that is 20 per cent of a total. Should its true cost be 60 per cent of the process average, its error on that operation cost is 40 per cent. But your over-all error would be 8 per cent (20×40).

Watch the proportions of standard minutes to the total for each process. You build up these totals from the work loads computed for Normal Volume (Chap. 10). There you laid out work loads by stations. Work loads are posted to process most easily in chart form (Fig. 34). This involves a helluva lot of detail I'm skipping over. But eventually you get the total work load for each of your processes.

EXPENSES TYPES

Now you can obtain Normal expenses from the curves you drew as outlined in Chap. 8. Read each curve separately at Normal Volume. Your next step is to find out what share of each element of Normal expense is caused by each process. In this study, conversion costs are similar to departmental burden rates. The difference is that the costs are analyzed and collected by processes lengthwise, so to speak, instead of crosswise or by little areas of production (Fig. 31).

In this analysis, you find that some charges to processes are direct. Often, jigs, patterns, and fixtures are made for specific products. Repairs of these are just as definite. Such costs should be charged directly to their processes, to reduce the errors of assignment.

Other expenses are indirect. They are of two types. Those that go with plant and equipment, you assign to processes by computation. Those like timestudy, planning, purchasing, and accounting, you analyze in detail to get their assignments to

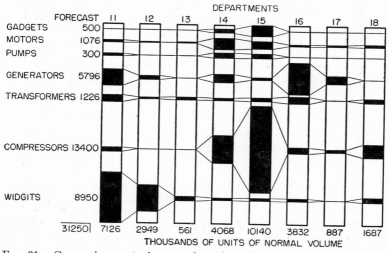

Fig. 31. Conversion costs in manufacturing often take sections of the facilities from several departments in combination.

processes. Let me remind you that these so-called overhead people work directly for the products—not for machines or departments.

ASSIGN EXPENSES

I will talk about this latter group first. I have two reasons. Primarily, it is in the proper assignment of these expenses that you will correct most of your errors in overhead costing. Then, too, these expenses are probably the bulk of your overhead.

The method is very simple. You take each account in turn and find out how much of it goes toward getting out each product. As you go about this analysis, you will see that you should have more reports and facts. But you don't have them now. So ask those who should know.

Go to the head of Production Control. Say to him, "John, you have 10 people in your group. Over the last 6 months, how did they spend their time?" He will start off, "Joe worked full time on motors. Jim spent half his time on pumps." It isn't as easy as I explain it. He will back and fill. But in time he will account for perhaps 80 per cent of his group.

PRODUCTION CONTROL						
	MOTORS	PUMPS	GENERAT.	TRANSF.	COMPRES.	PAYROLL
HEAD						
STENO						
CLERK	20	10	15	25	30	
JOE	100					
JIM		50	25	25		
CHARLIE				100		
FRED			50	50		
BILL			30		70	
GEORGE	20		80			
MAC	10	20		40	30	

Fɪɢ. 32. Analyze the work done by those in a staff function and set down the proportions of their time given to the production of your several products.

Go back over his statements. Ask if he has any figures to check against. Insist that you're talking about the last 6 months —not last week. After considerable effort, you will come up with a distribution about like Fig. 32.

Convert your analysis to money. Your starting figure is Normal expense. Let's use $48,000. In Fig. 33, you will see how this is spread. First, I took individual salaries. These show in the last column at the right. Each was assigned with the percentages of time estimated. When done, I added and spread in proportion the $10,900 not assigned. The totals by products are shown on the line marked "Normal Expense" at the bottom.

SORTED DISTRIBUTIONS

Other expenses may be distributed on more clear-cut bases. Take invoicing or order writing. You can start with the pieces of paper. Sort those for a representative period by products. Then count the number in each group. Don't count each as one unless the work in each is about the same. From such counts, you can assign by proportion your Normal expense. The money assignments for products that are combined in process groups can be

PRODUCTION CONTROL						
	MOTORS	PUMPS	GENERAT.	TRANSF.	COMPRES.	PAYROLL
HEAD						8000
STENO						2900
CLERK	700 / 20	350 / 10	525 / 15	875 / 25	1050 / 30	3500
JOE	5500 / 100					5500
JIM		2600 / 50	1300 / 25	1300 / 25		5200
CHARLIE				4800 / 100		4800
FRED			2400 / 50	2400 / 50		4800
BILL			1440 / 30		3360 / 70	4800
GEORGE	880 / 20		3520 / 80			4400
MAC	410 / 10	820 / 20		1640 / 40	1230 / 30	4100
TOT. ASSIGN.	7490	3770	9185	11015	5640	37100
DISTRIBUTED	2200	1090	2700	3250	1660	10900
NORMAL EXP.	9690	4860	11885	14265	7300	48000

FIG. 33. Distribute the wages of the function according to your analysis. Spread the amount left over that might be thought of as "overhead" in relation to the total directly assigned.

added later. This method is a good one to use wherever you can get such counts. And I would use it if it helped me to assign only part of an expense.

ENGINEERING COST

Among your indirect expenses is one you may not assign. If you have lots of "specials," why not look upon engineering as direct? Where many orders require application engineering, these costs are more correctly charged as direct labor instead of overhead. Such charges would have an engineering overhead of their own. You would determine this as we did for Production Control in Fig. 33.

I think this is the right approach even if it does not apply the bulk of your engineering. In saying this, I recognize that engineering may have little or lots of "research and development" in it. These are problems in themselves. Our concern here is that all costs we can get directly to the product will lessen the errors made by assignment.

MACHINE COSTS

Next, let's assign 13 expenses that grow out of having production equipment. These are divided into two groups:

1. Costs resulting from having equipment.
2. Costs resulting from having buildings.

The costs arising from equipment are often seven in number:

Depreciation	Maintenance material
Taxes	Connected horsepower
Insurance	Operation supplies
Maintenance labor	

Those caused by housing your equipment are six in number:

Depreciation	Insurance, building
Taxes, building	Maintenance labor
Taxes, land	Maintenance materials

These two groups totaling 13 expenses are all that can logically go into a machine burden rate. All other expenses can go directly to processes. This is an important distinction, to my way of thinking, when we seek cost control as contrasted with cost accounting. I will try to illustrate what I mean after we assign equipment depreciation as an example.

DEPRECIATION EXAMPLE

Probably, you have depreciation cards for each machine. If so, your task is easy. If not, I think you should have them to collect repair costs. You should know when to throw away a machine.

Set down your depreciation in the right-hand column (Fig. 34). Then spread each amount over the Normal work load that will be on that machine. Look at Drill Press. The depreciation of $120 is divided by 102,083 Units (standard minutes) and multiplied by 3,290 Units to get $4 for motors. Each is calculated in

MACHINE	UNITS	MOTORS	PUMP	GENERAT.	TRANSF.	COMPRES.	
DRILL	102083	3290	53438	25462	1272	18621	
W&S 2a	48752	8643	12431	10640	1632	15406	
BULLARD	34775	10432	8506	6431	— —	9406	
CINN MILL	35470	6932	4763	11407	8663	3705	
	221080	29297	79138	53940	11567	47138	

FIG. 34. Distribute each item of overhead cost assignable to a machine according to the Normal Volume assigned to that machine.

turn, or read off your slide rule. When all have been figured, you add vertically. In this way, you collect all the depreciation for Motors as $284 in our example. This is a very important detail.

MAINTAIN IDENTITY

Let me show you why, in greatly condensed form. Look at Fig. 35. This represents a type of cost-control sheet. Along its top are your accounts by responsibility. Down the left side are the products used in our examples, not yet combined in processes.

		LABOR			CHARGES				FIXED	
			PRODUC. CONTROL						DEPREC. EQUIP.	
MOTORS			9,690						284	
PUMPS			4,860						300	
GENERATORS			11,885						291	
TRANSFORMERS			14,265						95	
COMPRESSORS			7,300						274	
TOTAL			48,000						1,244	

FIG. 35. When each expense is unmixed with others, you can report the portions that belong to each product, keep the total in one place by responsibility, and show the relations of the portions to the total.

And while the distribution of the whole Production Control Department payroll looks silly alongside the Depreciation for four machines, those are illustrations only.

Here you see all the $48,000 payroll of Production Control. You see all the Depreciation. And, at the same time, you see their distributions to process groups. These are not buried under "forty 'leven" prorations. When you can see all of any one expense together, you have a workable basis for cost control. So follow the same pattern and distribute each expense unmixed with others.

REPLACEMENT DEPRECIATIONS

Before going on, I want to call your attention to depreciation costs. Your plant is like most, I would guess. Probably, you have some equipment bought in 1776 and some purchased yesterday. Probably, also, you show no depreciation cost at all for some equipment. It has been "written off." Undoubtedly, most of your depreciation charges are figured on purchased prices paid in 1945, 1940, and 1935 dollars. The foregoing conditions don't make sense to me. Why should your cost go up when you buy a new machine to replace an old one?

I believe that you should figure depreciation in terms of replacement costs to keep your control indicators set correctly. This is easy to do. For tax and bookkeeping purposes, you can carry your regular figures. But set up depreciations in terms of replacement costs. Then take the difference. Show this difference as an element of expense. In doing so, you will pull down your indicated profit to a more realistic figure. Then you can adjust it to legal status by a credit variance.

IN-BETWEEN EXPENSES

When you get to maintenance and power, you are on less sure footing. These are in a class between the arithmetic assignment like depreciation and the analytic approach used with Production Control.

You may have records that show maintenance charges by machines. That's fine. If you don't, you will want to start this kind of record. Later, you can correct your distribution. Maintenance is used here as an example of the type of expense you can and may later assign largely from recorded details.

Maybe you have departmental charge records. If so, work from these. See if you can get some help from supervisors of maintenance and production. If "they won't talk," make the best assignment you can to types of machines. Separate labor from materials. There are three reasons beyond our main point of trying for more accuracy:

1. Labor cost is more controllable than material cost.

2. Labor cost shifts to material when you replace instead of repair.

3. Labor cost shifts to charges (material) when you send out your maintenance work.

POWER CHARGES

Another method of assigning charges may be shown with power. Like those preceding, it is a substitute for facts when

1. You are starting without records you may institute.

2. You are continuing with assignments, where records do not pay for themselves.

Let's take horsepower that usually is not metered. First you survey the horsepower connected to your equipment. Then, by our two-way chart, you can assign this to processes. From the summary, you work up what I incorrectly call "power factors."

Your results should be in two parts. One reflects the stand-by charge you pay for being connected to utility power lines. I think of it as your share of their mortgage. This is the process portion of the constant charge. The other is the process share of the variable cost. Your answers might be anything but would resemble the following when set up for a monthly base:

	Constant	Activity
Motors............	50	.28
Pumps............	45	.32
Generators.........	32	.47
Transformers.......	20	.15
Compressors.......	40	.51

Notice that the "activity" rates seem inconsistent with the constants. I made them that way. You see activity is dependent upon your forecast of sales production. Hence you must approximate the probable use of connected power. Usage is what alters the variable part of expense.

You may work out a number of such factors for other expenses. To use them, you multiply current volume in standard time by the activity factors. Then add the constants to each. Add these sums, and you have weighted factors for assigning charges. You divide the sum of your weighted factors into the charge and pro-rate to the individual amounts included in your weighted total.

STANDARD-TIME BASIS

Finally, I come to the "direct-labor" base so commonly used. I put it last because so many use it to escape the work of analysis. We should use it, however, when analysis shows it to be the best method. Take Payroll as an instance. Analysis often shows that payroll work is practically proportional to direct-labor activity. General Supervision and Personnel may follow the same uniform rate. Use measured standard time when it is the influencing factor. But avoid grasping this basis just to avoid mental exercise.

In summary form, Fig. 36, you will see suggested bases for common expense assignment. I admit that I have hit the high spots. But we can't take the whole book to describe mechanics.

PRODUCTIVE ASSIGNMENT

In these several examples, we have skipped charging any expenses to the indirect departments. This may curl your hair. You argue, "The maintenance department uses power." "It does," I admit. And all your service departments take floor space. Again, the engineer looks at the solution differently.

Why not use a direct approach? Why not recognize that service departments cannot "earn" overhead? Only salable products that go out the door and stay out can earn overhead.

If you agree, then look at Fig. 37. The outside box depicts the whole plant. Inside is the productive part. It symbolizes the salable portion that can "earn" overhead. To illustrate, suppose my diagram typifies floor space. In this approach, I would over-

Expense	*Assigned*

Labor

Operating Labor:
  Direct Labor................. Direct analysis
  General Supervision.......... By analysis, unit basis
  Material Handling............ By analysis
  Trucking..................... By analysis
Maintenance Labor:
  Maintenance Buildings........ By area occupied
  Maintenance Machinery........ By analysis, machines used
  Maintenance Tools............ By ratio to tools used
General Labor:
  Engineers.................... By analysis
  Accounting................... By analysis, unit basis
  Planning..................... By analysis
  Payroll...................... Unit basis
  Timestudy.................... By analysis
  Watchmen..................... Area basis
  Personnel.................... Unit basis
  Laboratory................... By analysis
  Receiving.................... By analysis
  Stores....................... By analysis

Charges

Direct:
  Trucking..................... By labor analysis
  Power........................ By connected horsepower, unit activity
  Operation Supplies........... By analysis
  Light........................ Unit basis
  Heat......................... Unit basis, analysis
  Compensation Insurance....... Payroll
Maintenance:
  Maintenance Buildings........ By area occupied
  Maintenance Machinery........ Analysis of machines used
  Maintenance Tools............ By ratio to tools used
General:
  Engineer..................... By engineering labor
  Laboratory................... By laboratory labor
  Office Supplies.............. By office labor

Fixed

Depreciation Buildings....... By area occupied
Depreciation Machinery....... By machines used
Depreciation Tools........... By tools used
Taxes, Buildings............. By area occupied
Taxes, Machinery............. By tools used
Insurance, Buildings......... By area occupied
Insurance, Machinery......... By tools used

FIG. 36.   List of expenses with suggested method of distribution.

look that used by the service departments. I would assign productive floor space as we did our depreciation. And I would price the total assigned to each process at an inflated rate per square foot. To get the rate, I would divide my total area charge by the productive floor space only.

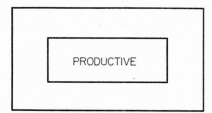

Fig. 37. Visualize all expenses as applied to the salable products. Only in that form can you collect the expenses from your customers.

TEST ACCURACY

Any expense assignment you make involves errors. Actually there is no such thing as accurate costs. Nothing is accurate except mathematical operations like 2×2. To obtain true costs in one two-plant company I know would call for approximately 1,600 conversion costs. Obviously, true-cost methods are impractical. We must develop conversion costs by products for economical costing and control. This means that items and products are grouped to give resulting conversion costs that are

1. Practical to apply to your many types of product.
2. Accurate within reasonable percentages of error.

"Accuracy within limits" means using an average. Now, we know an average is wrong. Haven't I been quarreling with this very thing through many pages? You ask quite naturally, "Then, why the change in attitude?" My reply is, "This is different." You laugh because you have heard that one before. But here is the difference. To approach the averages you should use, you first set your tolerance. If 5 per cent error is set as your limit, you will wind up with roughly twice as many conversion costs as if you set 10 per cent limits. You must prove your errors to be within your limits. In this way, you can shrink a relatively large number of conversion costs into a smaller number of groupings.

The cost of an average product is practically the same, computed by any method. Therefore, comparisons you want to make are of the extremes. The comparisons are between exact costs and conversion costs. Exact costs are determined by extending each operation in a series of extreme examples by labor plus the direct machine cost applicable. To this is added extension by the remainder of the process conversion costs times the Units or Standard Hours in the articles.

Such totals are compared with the conversion costs obtained as total process cost times total Units. The ratio of comparison is taken with the exact cost as the denominator. The variation from 100 per cent should not exceed the per cent you established as limiting. The reason is that costs at this point represent inventory values less material. Obviously, when material is added, your conversion costs will reflect a smaller per cent of error. For example, if the extreme variation of conversion cost from exact cost is 5 per cent and material equals half of the cost, your error is reduced to only 2.5 per cent.

COMBINING PROCESSES

If you took my earlier suggestion to separate each suspected difference, your accuracy tests will show small errors. Right off, you see that you may combine certain groups. By reducing the number, you save clerical cost of maintenance. However, there are two other factors to recognize. First, your combinations of products must be logical from the standpoint of usage. Second, you may not combine certain products with others because you will want to watch them. Certain products may be found to be unprofitable.

Manufacturing product groups should coincide with sales and administrative groups. Control and simplicity of routine costing are greatly improved when they can be the same. Therefore, before any combining of groups is done, you should make sure that no greater error in cost is made by using the total conversion cost including sales and administrative groups. You must retest your accuracy. The per cent of error must not exceed the limits you have set. When successive tests are made and the final groupings set up, your conversion costs are completed.

CHAPTER 13

WHY NOT STANDARDIZE YOUR COSTS?

"An enlightened willingness to change one's mind from hour to hour may be a fine thing in the academic atmosphere of any College or of any Court, but speaking as a practical business man, I can say 'It's a helluva way to run a railroad.' " [1]   In that comment on an entirely different subject, Benjamin Fairless says what I think of actual costs.

You can't tell how much you are drifting unless you set some stakes.   In industry we cannot set our course by the North Star. Our guideposts have to be standards of some kind.   "The modern concept of standard costs did not come from an accountant, it came from an engineer, Harrington Emerson," [2] according to C. E. Knoeppel.

STANDARD TIMES IN COSTING

Of course, standard costs for labor are easily obtained when you have standards for wage incentive.   I'm convinced that many incentive plans grew out of this very objective.   On the other hand, some plants that have had standard times with incentives for years do not have standard costs.   All their variances are buried in their actual costs and inventories.   Others, with time measures of output, persist in applying overhead by obsolete and incorrect methods.

These conditions may be the result of incomplete confidence in the standards.   Perhaps they exist because the accounting methods were introduced many years ago.   Whatever the explanation, there are clashes in reports.   Disagreements are unavoidable because differences will occur when costs are computed

[1] Fairless, Benjamin F., Guilty before Trial, address at Boston Jubilee, Mid-Century Celebration of Progress, May 8, 1950.

[2] Knoeppel, C. E., and E. G. Seybold, "Managing for Profit," p. 54, McGraw-Hill Book Company, Inc., New York, 1937.

by different methods. Cost reports that should aid management only confuse when there are two or more answers to a problem.

Evidence points toward the more extensive use of incentive standard times as the basis for cost controls. Notably, some accounting firms have added industrial engineers to their staffs. One controller I know has two engineers in his department. My belief is that this trend is in the right direction.[3]

GETTING STANDARDS

You can set your standards in two ways, suggests Stanley Henrici. "One is to build up the standard cost of each product; the other, to build up the standard cost of each operation." [4]   His are the accepted but by no means universal procedures.

Very few folks have set standards for costs. That is easy to understand. There are a great many plants that do not have standardized products. Later on, I will try to explain a third way that can provide most of the benefits of standard costs with either special or standard products.

Here, I want briefly to outline the accepted methods. These are based on the principle of fixing costs for labor, overhead, and material. To my way of thinking, the amounts are not so important as their fixing. Fixing points of comparison is the basic element in cost control.

STANDARD LABOR COST

In working toward standard costs, most people start with labor costs. So we'll begin there too.

You may work with operations or their totals by parts. That depends upon what you are after. My suggestion is that you need operation costs only when pricing inventory. You need part totals if you sell spare parts. And of course, you need totals for your assembled products.

Lacking time standards for your operations, you can pick out reasonable actuals to use. These may be either time or money. The arguments for using standard time were given in Chaps. 4

[3] Carroll, Phil, Where Cost Accounting and Industrial Engineering Meet, *The Journal of Accountancy,* April, 1949.

[4] Henrici, Stanley B., "Standard Costs for Manufacturing," p. 47, McGraw-Hill Book Company, Inc., New York, 1947.

and 6. Next in order comes piece rates, if you have them. These are standard costs in reality.

I hope you have standard times for your shop operations. You can use them for the other controls I've been talking about. You can work up standard costs directly from them. You should find all your standard times recorded on operation sheets of some type. Along with these may be shown the job-evaluation labor grades that apply to your operations. Multiplying these would give you "ideal" standard labor costs by operations.

Ideal costs should be tempered, in my opinion. There are losses due to

Waiting time	Shifts in personnel
Rework	Irregular materials
Setups	Failure to equal standard

Some portions of these are with us all the time. "Risks of business," I've heard them called. You should include some of these costs to make your standards more practical. Later on I will bring out some other phases of this inclusion.

STANDARD MATERIAL COSTS

Your standard material costs should be based on engineering specifications. They should include necessary scrap left in a strip when parts are blanked out on a punch press. In the same way, they include stock cut off and crop ends left when pieces are made on a screw machine. Your multipliers should be the standard material prices we discussed in Chap. 11.

How much scrap to include is a touchy subject. Reasonable amounts probably belong in standard cost for one reason. I think you should recognize the differences in hazards that some items have in comparison with others. But difference in scrap due to lot size should not be included, as I see it. I'm talking cost, not price, remember.

STANDARD OVERHEAD COST

To get a standard overhead cost, you have several choices. One is to multiply your standard times by a standard overhead rate. Another is to extend your standard labor cost by a standard overhead per cent. These may be machine, department, plant, or product overheads.

I'd use product conversion costs. In so doing, I would get "standard conversion costs" that included labor and overhead. That point confused Controller James Curtis, who asked, "Are you setting out to get standard costs?" This was at the start of an installation of conversion costs. He appeared disappointed when I answered, "Only indirectly."

COST MULTIPLIER

Now, with your indulgence, I'd like to sketch another form of "standard cost." In using the accepted type of standard costs, cost control is almost impossible. You must compile bushels of details for each period. When done, you can see variances from standard. But what caused these variances? Was it labor, material, or overhead? You can't tell without a lot of unscrambling. Yet, you must know the causes and the amounts if you are to gain control.

Oversimplified, your cost answer is the product of

$$\text{Quantity} \times \text{Rate}$$

Let me use cost to explain. If your labor is standardized, then a cost variation is caused by a rate variation. This leads to my question, "Why do all the multiplying? Why not control costs by controlling rates?"

Suppose you have 1.0 minute standard time for an operation or 12.0 minutes for a part. Also, assume that you use $1.80 per hour or $.03 per minute to figure your standard cost. Going on, let's take 200 per cent as overhead. Your standard cost then is

Operation: $1.0 \text{ min} \times \$.03 + 200\% = \$.09$

or

Part: $12.0 \text{ min} \times \$.03 + 200\% = \$1.08$

Should your labor rate go up to $.04 per minute for any reason, the rise in your cost will be $.04 − $.03 times your standards.

Operation: $1.0 \text{ min} \times \$.01 = \$.01$

or

Part: $12.0 \text{ min} \times \$.01 = \$.12$

"Wait a minute," you say. "You forgot the overhead." No, I didn't. Your overhead did not rise in the example. And if you falsely charge overhead to an increase in labor cost, you have "overabsorbed" burden. Of course, such a rise couldn't earn overhead even if you did incorrectly charge it. Besides, such a method is only a habit. Your actual overhead rate per dollar of labor would drop if you were to carry through the whole process. On a standard-time basis, it would not change in this case.

OVERHEAD MULTIPLIER

Now let's assume an increase in overhead rate instead of wage rate. Suppose your overhead rate goes up from 200 to 300 per cent. Your rise in cost will be 300 − 200 times your labor costs.

Operation: $1.0 \times \$.03 \times 100\% = \$.03$

or

Part: $12.0 \times \$.03 \times 100\% = \$.36$

Notice that, in both labor and overhead rises, I set down the increases as Base × Increase in rates. My purpose was to show

AUGUST VOLUME 1,852,000 UNITS

	ENGINEERING	PLANNING	TIMESTUDY	ACCOUNTING	PERSONNEL
"STANDARD"	9.12	1.67	4.43	4.06	1.39
ACTUAL	11.53	1.45	4.86	3.92	1.28
GAIN OR LOSS	+2.41	−.22	+.43	−.14	−.11
DOLLARS @ 1852M					
GAIN		407.44		259.28	203.72
LOSS	4463.32		796.21		

FIG. 38. This section of a report shows the "rates" of expenses per 1,000 units of standard time. These combine variations in dollars with those of volume. Comparisons of such rates with "standards" tell immediately what happens to product costs.

that you can find out what your variances are from the changes in rates—in multipliers. That is what I'm driving at here. This is the other method I said could be used where your "rates" become the standard costs you measure against. This method will show you where the variances are without wading through thousands of operation or part costs. You can see how much you have gained or lost before you make all such calculations.

Look at Fig. 38 as an example. Suppose the function rates per 1,000 Units (standard minutes) shown are parts of your overhead conversion cost. In this form, you have two advantages not provided in any other method I know:

1. You can see where your costs change and how much. You can place responsibility where it belongs.

2. You can determine your gains and losses by accountabilities without vast quantities of computations.

These features impress me because I think speed of reporting is essential. More importantly, by this method you can put your finger on the weak spots. Having these two elements of cost control, you are in a position to take correct action.

CHAPTER 14

CALL ATTENTION TO VARIANCES

You cannot gain control of costs until you know where the leaks are. These are shown in what are called "variances." Variances are differences. They are plus or minus differences between actuals and whatever you use as base-line measures. They are signals that call for management action. They supply the means for applying what is called the "management by exception principle."

Control by variances is both effective and unique. Variance control is unique because you rarely find a manager who can tell you where the money is made and lost, and how much. If he is aware of the facts, you can be reasonably sure he does not know why. Few managers can tell you how much of a result is due to cost, price, or volume. Sometimes they have a feel. Sometimes they think they know the answers. But seldom are the actual variances sorted out. How can they know?

HUNDREDS OF VARIANCES

One reason why is that you have hundreds of variances. You can show variances for every detail you have set some measure for. "That's too much detail," you hear. Maybe so. Keep in mind, however, that when you make groupings you bury whatever variances offset each other.

Repeating myself, "variances are signals that call for management action." Here we have two elements of control. First is action. I put action first because figures and systems are lifeless. They are costly. They make your profit picture worse instead of better if you get no action.

Second is amount or degree. You can have degree of action, or lack of it, in control. You can have degree or amount of variance. I put these together because we humans will get excited sometimes only if amounts are big enough.

TYPES OF VARIANCE

You will have large variances, if you have just started budgets. You will discover them in unexpected places. You can roughly group them in types of variance as due to five factors:

1. *Performance* variance is the difference between actual expense and budget, or standard if you have standards.

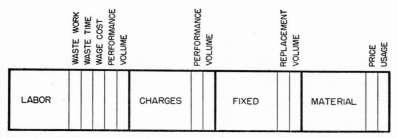

FIG. 39. Variances often show up as excess costs and may be caused by different types of conditions.

2. *Material* variance arises out of changes in both price of material and amount used.

3. *Replacement* depreciation variance is a pet figure of mine. I included it to show how far costs are off because your equipment is partially obsolete either in design or in price.

4. *Price* variance is what you get when you sell products at varying prices.

5. *Volume* variance is the very important effect in cost and profit or loss caused by shifts in amount of business.

All these types of variances can have major influences on your profit or loss statement. They are indicated on Fig. 39. I will discuss each as we come to it.

PERFORMANCE VARIANCE

Let's start with performance variances. These are the usual type. Many folks report them now because they have budgets. Such variances can be large, as I tried to say in Chap. 9. To emphasize this point, I have sketched a relation in Fig. 40.

Certain of these variances you can assign wholly to the sales organization. Others, you lay on the doorstep of the manufacturing division. Some, of course, are to be found in both. Hence, you should think of variances as falling into two main groups, namely, selling and manufacturing. This distinction is important. You must consider the time lag between these two parts of cost control. The time lag may be small or great. This lag is the time difference between the sales and the manufacturing efforts. Obviously, you should measure each set of expenses against its own volume index.

With this separation in mind, you can expect your costs to differ from their budgets. You will see these variances when

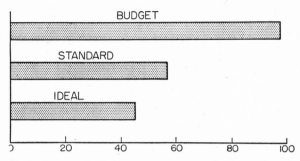

Fig. 40. Budgets may include excess expenses because they have been set up in terms of past performances.

you set down actual expenses against budgets. These budgets you compute to conform exactly with volume for the current period. Then you draw off the variances.

These variances point out how well expenses have been managed. Savings will occur when your actual costs are under the budgets. Excesses will be losses. Control begins when the boss asks for and receives logical explanations of the causes of variances. This is how you start to work the dynamics of control.

MONTHLY REPORT

Let's take a look at a report of a month's operations for a small concern on Fig. 41. The budget amounts were computed for the actual volume of business done. They are strictly comparable with actual expenses. The amounts differ for manufacturing and sales because of the effects of seasonal demand. "Shipping" is included in sales expense because goods sold have more of an influence. Incidentally, this budget report carries 6

	JULY			AUGUST			
Volume 1000 Units	402			436			
	Budget	Actual	Var	Budget	Actual	Var	Budg
						MANUFACTURING	
LABOR							
Direct Labor	10832	10423	− 409	11556	10920	− 636	
Indirect Labor	531	504	− 27	564	587	+ 23	
Maint. Bldg. & Equip.	1406	1395	− 11	1446	1410	− 36	
Laboratory	591	602	+ 11	605	600	− 5	
Gen. Supervision	534	530	− 4	543	578	+ 35	
Janitor & Watchman	381	414	+ 33	386	404	+ 18	
Standards & Cost	527	486	− 41	551	484	− 67	
Loading labor	731	725	= 6	762	810	± 48	
	15533	15079	− 454	16413	15793	− 620	
CHARGES							
Maint. Bldg. & Equip.	2029	2145	+ 116	2119	2191	+ 72	
Operation Supplies	1021	1102	+ 81	1108	1156	+ 48	
Power	4660	4591	− 69	4840	4775	− 65	
Steam	2562	2485	− 77	2627	2489	− 138	
Compensation Ins.	641	602	− 39	651	573	− 78	
Indirect Supplies	651	697	± 46	703	693	= 10	
	11564	11622	+ 58	12048	11877	− 171	
FIXED							
Depreciation	2950	2950	0	2950	2950	0	
Taxes	930	930	0	930	930	0	
Insurance	50	50	0	50	50	0	
	3930	3930	0	3930	3930	0	
Total Manufacturing	31027	30631	− 396	32391	31600	− 791	
						SALES & ADMINISTRATIVE	
Volume 1000 Units	430			450			
SALES & ADVER.							
Salary & Comm.	2705	2820	+ 115	2742	2804	+ 62	
Travel	443	460	+ 17	456	461	+ 05	
Tele. & Stationery	553	511	− 42	574	536	− 38	
Samples	510	462	− 48	494	506	+ 12	
Printing	3021	2807	− 214	3046	2959	− 87	
	7232	7060	− 172	7312	7266	− 46	
SHIPPING							
Labor	1158	1096	− 62	1198	1186	− 12	
Cartage	4398	4412	+ 14	4607	4580	− 27	
	5556	5508	− 48	5805	5766	− 39	
ADMINISTRATIVE							
Administrative	1392	1353	− 39	1395	1338	− 57	
Legal	160	140	− 20	161	201	+ 40	
General	345	362	+ 17	359	327	= 32	
Total Sales &	1897	1855	− 42	1915	1866	− 49	
Administrative	14685	14423	− 262	15032	14898	− 134	

Fɪɢ. 41. Monthly budget report may be made to show variances by **expense** accounts so that control is related to responsibilities.

months on the same sheet. That is a good idea. You want **to** see if you are making progress.

Notice that some variances are negative. You see a sizable gain in Direct Labor for both July and August. If these are realities, you want to reproduce such gains frequently in the future. These are evidences of progress in cost reduction. You should meet the budget and go below it. This is especially emphasized if your expense budgets are determined from past, uncontrolled experiences. You should expect that, as control improves, each repetition of a given volume will show lower expense than you had previously. Each year, you should be able to redraw many expense curves at lower levels.

Other variances are plus. Look at Maintenance and Sales Salaries for July. These are the kind you must "turn the heat on." You must make every effort to determine causes so that such losses will not be repeated. Usually, excess costs point to a lack of proper supervision. In such cases, you will have to teach the supervisors how to be businessmen. You will want to show them how to stay within their budgets.

DIRECT LABOR

Now to go into the finer detail, let's examine a direct labor report. Figure 42 is an example. This is an analysis for 1 week.

At the left are standards per 1,000 Units (standard minutes). These, multiplied by the production of 76,481 Units, equal the "standard dollars." Actual dollars show in the second column. Variances are recorded in the two columns at the right. Such details show losses to be $382 instead of $341 that a summary report would reflect.

Reports like this can be issued within 2 days after the end of the period. And details can be kept in time. They need not be converted into money until the end of the period. Even then, they can be kept in time if the supervisors better understand time reports.

QUICK REPORTING

As control improves, you will see one of the important advantages you derive from budgets. You can get control information while it is "still hot." This is a decided contrast from the usual timing of cost information given to a supervisor. Often, his expense reports get to him weeks—sometimes months—after the money has been spent. Then it is much too late to do anything about it. Post-mortems are a waste of time. While your super-

Direct Labor, Department 16						
		Week of October 24, 1951				
Production Units 76,481	Standard per 1,000 Units	Dollars			Variance	
		Actual	Standard	Excess	Credit
Productive.....	$(21.50)	$1,815.51	$1,644.34	$171.17	
Waiting........	(.43)	21.77	32.89	...	$11.12
Fall Down.....	(.00)	86.02	.00	86.02	
Setup..........	(2.81)	184.34	214.91	...	30.57
Expense........	(.32)	45.62	24.47	21.15	
Prod. Indirect..	(.14)	45.58	10.71	34.87	
Trucking.......	(.48)	77.24	36.71	40.53	
Supervision.....	(1.26)	125.06	96.37	28.69	
	$(26.94)	$2,401.14	$2,060.40	$382.43	$41.69

Check $ 2,401.14 $ 382.43
               −2,060.40   − 41.69

            $ 340.74 $ 340.74

Fig. 42. Subdivide major expenses into smaller details when you want to find out where the leaks are.

visor is trying to dig up alibis for what happened then, his expenses are slipping now.

With the kind of budget we are talking about here, a supervisor can be told in advance. You can say that the volume will be so much and his expenses should not exceed specified amounts. These forecasts may be for the coming week in some instances and the coming month in others. Given sufficient notice to arrange his work accordingly, he has an even chance to control his expenses.

MATERIAL—PRICE VARIANCE

Then you have variances in material. You recognize that material costs vary. If you have been using job-costing methods, you have seen wide fluctuations in costs for different lots. But have you attempted to show why the costs of materials shift from one lot to the next? There are two major reasons.

First is the variance due to price. It can vary all over the lot. It is influenced by

Purchasing skill	Inventory planning
Engineering standards	Sales forecasting

Price variance is the difference between the prices you paid for materials and the standard prices set for those materials. And this control can uncover a gold mine. So much depends upon what you set up as standard prices. We discussed these in Chap. 11.

What I have in mind here is the long-range development from where you happen to be to where you could be with better controls. Take engineering standards, as an example. How many different nuts, bolts, and washers do you buy? How would your costs improve if you could buy larger quantities of fewer designs?

Then, of course, prices change. And all these factors are beyond the control of the shop. So price variance should be separated from material cost. It is computed by pricing material invoices at the standard prices adopted for normal costs.

MATERIAL USAGE VARIANCE

The other material variance depends upon material usage. Your normal cost of material is what it should take to produce an article. Then your material usage variance is any excess materials over your standard amounts figured at the standard prices you adopt for normal or "standard costs."

Naturally, a variance occurs when the shop uses more material than it should. Scrap and defective materials are important amounts. As I suggested in Chap. 13, your standard amounts should include necessary scrap like the skeletons of strips in punch-press work. In the same way, I believe you should include some scrap allowance for castings. This should not be a uniform percentage taken arbitrarily. Some castings are much more hazardous to make than others. These difficulties ought to be recognized just as you would distinguish between products made of aluminum or steel. Our concern is twofold. One is to fix responsibility for cost control. The other is to determine product profitability.

Loss in yield is another material usage variance to watch. And some shops have large losses when they substitute materials. If substitution causes major losses, these should be reported separately. Usually they are not the shop's fault. They stem from poor planning or purchasing. Often from sales pressures. Also, they are created in some plants because they can't afford to stock every proper sized material. The variance here is like that of not making tools for small lots. It should be kept separate to balance against the purported savings made by not stocking the correct size. This saving can easily become an important loss with changes in product mix.

REPLACEMENT VARIANCES

Now my pet again. As I pointed out in Chap. 12, probably your company is operating with some fully depreciated equipment. Also, probably your plant is using equipment that was purchased before prices were inflated. Ralph Kraut says that 43 per cent of our equipment is obsolete.[1] As a result, you get costs that are lower than they should be. Your profits are fictionally high. In different words, you will raise costs when you replace machinery.

You should guard against this sort of bookkeeping change. My recommendation was to set up depreciation in terms of replacement costs. Here you should show the difference between modernized costs and those carried on your books. Call it some term like "replacement variance." This variance will change with three different conditions:

[1] Kraut, Ralph J., New Production Facilities, *Mechanical Engineering,* March, 1952.

1. Changes in volume.
2. Rises in replacement costs.
3. Shifts from replacement to actual depreciation.

PRICE VARIANCE

Now we come to two variances that are largely sales department responsibilities. These are price and volume. We will talk about price variance first.

If you manufactured only one article, priced at $1, and always sold it at $1, you would have no variance due to price. But if you sold some at 90 cents, then your variance would be 10 cents apiece for the number sold at 90 cents. But your problem is not nearly so simple. You have many products. And if yours include many specials, you don't even have a price list to go by.

But you do have conversion costs and normal selling prices. In Chap. 10, we priced the normal volume. These prices by lines of products less the normal materials content will give you normal selling prices of conversion. Mixed in such answers will be varying profits and losses.

Taking the long-range view again, there is a better approach. Take your conversion costs as determined (Chap. 12). Add to these the profits you should make. Then establish what you might call standard conversion prices per 1,000 Units (standard minutes) or per Standard Hour.

Your price variance for any period then is the difference between your standards for conversion and what you sell conversion for. This is fairly easy to get at if you keep materials separate as shown in Method C, Chap. 5. You build up Units or Standard Hours sold and new sales income less standard materials by products groups. Alongside you place the standard conversion prices multiplied by Units or Standard Hours sold. The differences are your price variances.

Price variances are controls extremely useful to progressive managements. They point the trend lines of results you should get from two major sources. First is the change from sales dollar to conversion pricing. Second is the shift from average overhead costing to conversion costing. Both of these show up certain products as losing money. Ordinarily, you do not correct these conditions overnight. As you make progress, your price variances will improve.

VOLUME VARIANCE

After you have sorted out the price variance, you should compute the effects of volume change. This is a mixed effect. Your several product volumes move in different cycles. You would have difficulty in isolating the true effects.

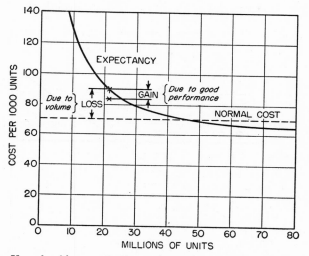

Fig. 43. You should separate the variance due to volume from that due to performance.

The point is that your milling machine works on whatever products happen to be going through the plant. Your superintendents, accountants, and engineers apply their efforts to the products at hand.

But you can get a bulk figure easily. You can compute it from the "constant expenses" you found in Chap. 9. The responsibilities for its control are mixed. You cannot logically criticize your plant manager for all increases in overhead ratio when the sales department has failed to provide production volume. In contrast, you should not compliment your works manager for all reductions in costs when the sales department has filled the plant.

For control purposes then, you want to know whether actual conversion costs change as they should with volume. You may see what I'm driving at by studying Fig. 43.

If you divide a curve of expense by a number of different volumes, you obtain a curve of cost per unit of volume. Your cost at normal volume would be one of those points. Then, if you draw a line across the curve representing normal cost per unit, you portray a kind of break-even point. At all volumes less than normal, the cost per unit will probably be higher than the normal cost. Likewise, at all volumes above normal, the cost per

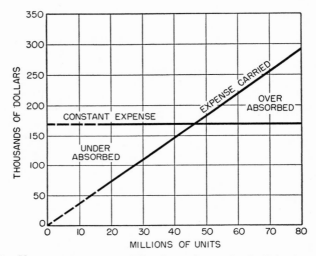

Fig. 44. Your constant cost of "nucleus of organization" is the expense that determines the variance due to volume.

unit may be expected to be lower than the normal cost. The difference between the straight line of normal cost and the curve of probable cost at any volume is a profit or loss per unit due solely to volume.

Chances are that your actual cost at any current volume will not strictly conform with the curve of expected cost at that volume. The actual cost may be above or below the curve. When it is above the curve, your actual cost is higher than was expected. When it is below the curve, your actual cost reflects better control. To see dollar gains or losses, take a look at Fig. 44. This typifies what happens with the constant in every expense that has one. Your volume variances are like those indicated. You can compute them in total or by account. The portion of any constant carried at a current volume is

$$\text{Amount Carried} = \frac{\text{Actual Volume}}{\text{Normal Volume}} \times \text{Constant}$$

The difference between the Constant and the Amount Carried, gain or loss, is your variance.

BOOKKEEPING PROFIT AND LOSS

Most operating statements mix the variances due to performance and to volume in one net figure. Notice in Fig. 43 how a

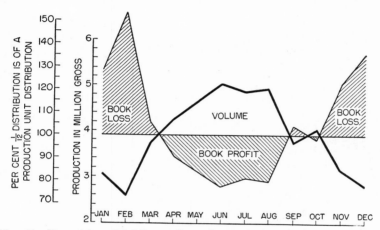

FIG. 45. Do not be misled by profits or losses that result from bookkeeping. These should be corrected by variance reports and accrual accounting.

performance gain offsets a volume loss. Now examine Fig. 45. You will see how change in volume causes a simple arithmetic or bookkeeping change in profit or loss. These curves show the effects of habitually charging one-twelfth of the constant expense to the current month. This first came to my attention about 1925. I walked into Ben Mitchell's office one morning and asked, "How did last month turn out?" He said, "Fine—but it doesn't mean anything. You see, this is our busy season." Six months or so later, I made about the same inquiry. This time his reply was, "Terrible—but it doesn't mean much. This is our dull season."

Now I ask you, "If the monthly operating statement is off so far that it means nothing to the manager, shouldn't you change it?" It seems to me that the obvious answer is "Yes."

The variations due to volume should be isolated from changes due to managerial control, or lack of it. Mixing these two in one figure of loss or profit is very misleading.

VARIANCE SUMMARY

After you isolate your variances, you should bring them all together. As an example, for March, you might show the following:

Variance	Loss	Gain
Direct Labor...........	$3,046	
Indirect Labor.........	...	$ 4,209
Charges...............	...	871
Replacement...........	903	
Material Price.........	...	633
Material Usage........	157	
Sales.................	...	1,044
Administrative........	...	398
Volume...............	...	3,118
Price.................	1,682	
	$5,788	$10,273
Net.................	...	$ 4,485

You need variance segregations like these to show how you are progressing. You need these in enough detail to measure the actions of those responsible for results.

HIGHER MANAGERS

On this, Charlie James says, "To speak of the 'behavior of accounts,' as many do, is to look at the shadow and overlook the substance. The figures merely mirror men—their motives and their responsibilities." [2]

You want to hold each supervisor responsible for managing his work. These men, in turn, should look to their lieutenants for results. This suggests that reports of results be grouped as you move upward in management responsibilities. Progressively,

[2] James, Charles C., Efficient Planning for Budgeting, *Advanced Management,* September, 1949.

you can group actual expenses, budgets, and variances in increasingly larger subtotals for convenience in presentation. The superior need not know the details. The details can be made available upon request. The point is that he must expect and get satisfactory answers to his questions of, "Why this rise—or decline?" The top executive can be kept informed of progress with as few as five or six key trend figures.

Joe Chester, a plant manager I know, states the way control should work. He says, "I see the results of the month's operations before they arrive at headquarters. My job is to determine answers to the questions headquarters is sure to ask before they ask them." His discerning analysis emphasizes the difference between controlled costs and happenstance costs. Control is effective when those responsible for costs are made aware of the causes of expense variances and trained to take action to control them. The more nearly you can get actual costs to approach ideal costs, the greater will be the success, both individual and company.

CHAPTER 15

BREAK-EVEN POINTS ARE HIGH

We all think of lowered unit costs resulting from increases in volume. Many of us believe this is due to the proration of "fixed costs." Actually, this "fixed costs" is a misleading term. So-called fixed costs are relatively small in the average plant.

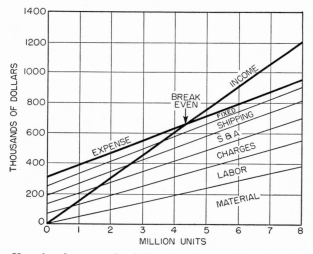

FIG. 46. Your break-even point is largely influenced by the constant cost of your organization.

The big element affected by volume is what I have called the cost to keep the doors open—cost of the nucleus of an organization. The bulk of this cost is wages and salaries. For example, in one organization "fixed costs" were only 15 per cent of the "constant cost" at zero volume.[1] In another company, the variable part of all wage and salary cost is but 54 per cent

[1] Carroll, Phil, Break-even Points, *Modern Management*, July, 1949.

at normal volume. The remaining 46 per cent is a constant labor cost regardless of volume. Of course, these percentages would change for different volumes. Figure 46 shows almost the same per cent relation.

You can see how this happens. Your invoice writers do just about the same typing whether your customers order 100 or 1,000 pieces. Setups you make to turn out production cost you roughly the same whether your lot sizes are small or large. Your sweeper does nearly the same work whether there is low or high volume.

PROFIT GRAPH

The large constant expense you have makes for a flatter slope of the total cost line in relation to volume. On a graph, your total expense line will cross your income line at some volume. This is known as the break-even point. Break-even means no profit, no loss. Beyond this point, profits before taxes show on the "profit graph" as the spread between income and expense. The break-even point shows up only because income equals expense at some volume of business.

Obviously, every increase in cost raises the break-even point. Fred Gardner reports on this for 1,000 companies representing "almost 75 per cent of the volume of manufacturing business done in this country. Before the war, those companies broke even at 55 per cent of their average yearly sales output for the combined years 1936 to 1939. Above the Break-even Point, they produced a profit of $27 per $100 of net sales. . . . Today (November, 1949), those companies break even at 115 per cent of the 1935–9 capacity raised to present selling prices, and instead of picking up $27, they now average $16 per $100 of net sales." [2]

Also, every reduction in price raises your break-even point except when you have an offsetting expansion in volume. And be careful—we fool ourselves sometimes with optimism. I know of one instance where it would have required a 150 per cent increase in volume to get back a proposed 5 per cent reduction in price.

[2] Gardner, Fred V., Management Looks at the Break-even Point, p. **17**, *Proceedings*, SAM Conference, November, 1949.

FICTITIOUS PROFITS

Naturally, we work toward lower prices through better methods—greater productivity. That is where our high standard of living comes from. Yet every time we get somebody's savings to invest in tools and equipment, we raise the constant portion of cost. We may also raise the break-even point.

Profits are becoming more necessary to obtain funds for expansion and replacement. Less is being supplied by investors perhaps because profits are not enough. At the same time, we read newspaper blasts about "exorbitant profits," "share-the-wealth," and "ability to pay."

Much of reported profits are fictitious. They are inflated because depreciation charges are based on equipment and plant costs prior to the 52-40 formula. You may be extremely embarrassed as your depreciation costs are raised through replacements in equipment at current prices. That is why I brought in the "replacement depreciation" mentioned earlier.

MATERIAL CONTENT

You must know that your break-even point shifts. One major cause you may have overlooked is the change in product mix. The expense line rises or falls as the costs of products sold change in proportion. So does the income line. Hidden within these shifts are several variables. Material content is one. Profit margins is another. Let's take a look at these two at this point.

Suppose we think of three different companies selling the same product instead of one company selling three products. My assumption is easier to portray correctly. And to show the effects of material content, let's suppose that each company manufactures different portions of the products it sells.

Firm A makes all of its product.
Firm B makes half and buys half.
Firm C buys all of its product.

In our first illustration, all three firms sell $260,000 worth of goods per year. Their expenses are built up according to my assumption. These are shown on Fig. 47. The major variable of material is set apart as "Purchased Product."

Naturally, you will need less equipment and organization when you buy a large portion of your product. That means your constant cost goes down. But your expense per sales dollar goes

FIRMS SELLING SAME PRODUCT BUT MAKING DIFFERENT PORTIONS OF
CONVERSION

	Firm A, 100%		Firm B, 50%		Firm C, 0%	
	Constant	Variable	Constant	Variable	Constant	Variable
Material..............	0	50,000	0	25,000	0	0
Labor.................	2,000	50,000	1,000	25,000	0	0
Overhead.............	32,000	66,000	16,000	33,000	0	0
Shipping.............	1,000	18,000	500	9,000	0	0
Purchased Product.....	0	0	0	105,000	0	210,000
Administration and Sales.	12,000	42,000	11,000	36,000	10,000	31,000
Total Expense.........	47,000	226,000	28,500	233,000	10,000	241,000
Sales Income...........	...	260,000	...	260,000	...	260,000
Profit at 260,000 Sales....	...	34,000	...	27,000	...	19,000
% Profit on Sales Dollars.	...	13.1	...	10.4	...	7.3

Fɪɢ. 47. The proportion you manufacture of what you sell has an important effect on your constant costs and, hence, on your break-even point.

up. You have to pay profits to your suppliers. These differences are reflected in the equations of my expense lines.

Firm A, Total Expense = \$47,000 + \$.688 per Sales Dollar
Firm B, Total Expense = \$28,500 + \$.786 per Sales Dollar
Firm C, Total Expense = \$10,000 + \$.888 per Sales Dollar

Now let's see how these conditions affect the break-even points. We know they will shift.

BREAK-EVEN SHIFTS

Your break-even point is that volume where the income equals the outgo. That is where sales equal expense—where our two lines cross.

On our profit graph, the slope of the sales line is \$1 per \$100. We have no constant. If we set down the sales line equation as equal to the expense line equation, then for Firm A we get

$$\$1.0 \times \text{Volume} = \$47,000 + \$.688 \times \text{Volume}$$

Transposing

$$(1.0 - .688) \times \text{Volume} = \$47,000$$

$$\$.312 \text{ Volume} = \$47,000$$

$$\text{Break-even Volume} = \$151,000$$

By the same method, you can find all three break-even volumes. They are:

	Break-even Volume
Firm A...........	$151,000
Firm B...........	133,000
Firm C...........	89,000

It would appear that you are better off if you buy most of your products. I don't think so. If your supplier can make a profit, you ought to be able to do better than he can in your own business. But let's go on to profit margin.

PRICE REDUCTION

Maybe I can best portray varying profit margins by reducing selling prices in our three little companies. To bring out the change, we will start with the factors that influence our profits as they now are.

	Firm A	Firm B	Firm C
Constant..................	$47,000	$28,500	$10,000
Profit....................	34,000	27,000	19,000
	$81,000	$55,500	$29,000
At $260,000 per $1.00 sales..	$ .312	$ .213	$ .112

In Firm A, each dollar of income contributes $.312 toward profit. First it offsets the constant cost. Then after we pass the break-even point, it adds up to make profit.

Now if we reduce our sales price, our sales dollar is less than a dollar. Whatever we cut off our prices comes off these "contributions" toward profits. Let's take off 5 per cent as a starter. Figure 48 shows the results.

Firm A has an income of $.312 less $.050 equals $.262 per dollar of sales. And to make the same dollar profit as before, we must increase sales. The amount of increase is $.050/$.262, or

VOLUME REQUIRED TO OFFSET PRICE REDUCTION

	Firm A, 100%	Firm B, 50%	Firm C, 0%
5% REDUCTION IN SELLING PRICE			
Income per Dollar of Sales........	$.312	$.213	$.112
Reduction in Selling Price........	.050	.050	.050
Remaining Income............	$.262	$.163	$.062
Increase in Volume Required......	.050/.262	.050/.163	.050/.062
Per Cent Increase...............	19	31	81
10% REDUCTION IN SELLING PRICE			
Income per Dollar of Sales........	$.312	$.213	$.112
Reduction in Selling Price........	.100	.100	.100
Remaining Income............	$.212	$.113	$.012
Increase in Volume Required......	.100/.212	.100/.113	.100/.012
Per Cent Increase...............	47	89	833

FIG. 48.   Your working margin goes down as you reduce the amount of conversion your company actually does and the effect of price change is much more drastic.

19 per cent.   If Firm A drops its price 10 per cent, we will need 47 per cent more sales to get even again.   But see what happens with Firm C.   We will have to raise volume 833 per cent.   Maybe you can see these changes better in Fig. 49.   These compare our starting conditions with the 5 per cent price reduction only.

VOLUME FETISH

Remember that I drew the latter graphs to show the effects of differing profit margins on the break-even point.   In the next chapter, I will attempt to emphasize this factor as it bears on over-all profit with mixed products.

Continuing with price reduction, let me say first, "I believe in it." Nothing bothers me quite so much as price pegging and subsidies. I can't see the difference between "fair-trade" price control and cartel or monopoly restraints. How can we actually

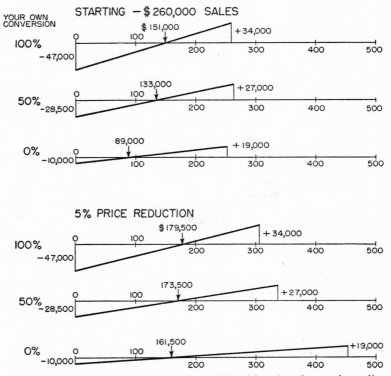

FIG. 49. Notice how break-even points shift with price change depending upon how much of what you sell is manufactured in your own plant.

raise standards of living unless relative prices come down? My reasoning tells me that price reductions should follow cost reductions.

Notice, I say "follow cost reduction." I'm leading up to the treacheries of price cutting as the means of securing greater volume. You have seen in Fig. 49 what happens with this approach. Melvin Copeland says, "In my experience, one of the most widespread fallacies encountered in economics and business pertains to the assumed economics of large-scale operations." [3]   He's talking about empire building. But only the goal differs from the fetish of more volume.

If you lose a nickel on each one you sell and you sell enough of them, you'll go broke. Volume of itself cannot solve an unprofitable condition. Added volume must add to profit. Sure, there are economies in larger volume. But they can't show up as profit if you give them away. You can give away profit in price reduction. You can spend your economies in sales costs added to take business away from your competitors.

WATCH CONSTANT COSTS

Volume by itself is not the answer. It is not the cure-all that some folks seem to think it is. You have to make progress through cost reduction, as I see it. Then you can reduce prices and enlarge your markets, your volume, and your profits.

Cost reduction comes through better methods of doing what you have to do. You get even more constructive results when you eliminate things you don't have to do. Both will lower your break-even point until you pass some savings on to your customers. Then you may raise it again.

I hedge in the last statement because you can markedly affect your break-even point by what you do to your constant cost. Your constant causes your break-even point. Observe how much lower Firm C's break-even point is than Firm A's. And remember that the bulk of your constant cost is wages and salaries. Its size depends upon two main factors:

1. How well you control expenses as volume shrinks and expands.

2. How much you spend on being stylish—optional and luxury items.

You can see that profit could be made at any volume if it were possible wholly to eliminate your constant costs. That is impossible, of course. But because perfection is not attainable is no reason why we can't do more than we have. Considerably more effort can be made to change constant costs than is usually evidenced. Almost any reduction should lower the break-even

[3] Copeland, Melvin T., "The Executive at Work," p. 40, Harvard University Press, Cambridge, Mass., 1951.

point. Thus you can increase the range in volume that produces profits.

One caution before we leave this subject. Keep in mind that the profit graph depicts only one static condition. Yet it does indicate what you can expect from policy changes. In general, you can improve profits and lower your break-even point by

Reducing variable costs.
Reducing constant expenses.
Reducing unprofitable sales.

CHAPTER 16

PLUG YOUR SALES-PROFIT LEAKS

If we look behind the profit graph, we can find many profit leaks. We can divide these into two main groups:

1. Leaks caused by excess costs.
2. Leaks resulting from short income.

Those arising from incorrect costing I plan to cover in our next chapter. At this point, I want to discuss briefly ways we lose or cut down on income. One shows up in what we call order quantity. Another grows out of special services we may give our customers. Then also, there is that basic question, "Who pays the freight?"

COST PER ORDER

We know that it costs several dollars to run an order through our office "paper mill." Consequently, we have a break-even point on an order. I suggested to one client, "It would be cheaper to give the bolts to your customers than to charge for them."

Your cost per order may be almost any amount. So much depends upon how you figure it. If your salespeople are order takers, you may include their costs. Ordinarily, we think of the costs of order interpreting and writing, addressing and mailing, invoicing and collecting. You should include process setups by all means if they occur per order.

Your cost per order may be in the range of $2 to $5. In Washington they run higher. "The cost of putting through each purchase order averaged in the Treasury Department, $7.06; in the Bureau of the Mint, the cost was $13.98; and in the U.S. Coast Guard, $23.94. In the Interior Department the average cost was $9.95 per order." [1]

[1] High, Stanley, In Washington It's Waste As Usual, *The Reader's Digest,* July, 1951.

163

I can understand such figures. I had an experience with the Navy. They wanted a Discussion Leader's Manual costing $2.00. First came forms requesting a quotation. Then came an order written in ditto. So there were multiple copies. When I sent an invoice, it came back with a request for several copies. At this point I wrote, "Please cut out the routine if you order again. Send a check, and I'll send the material."

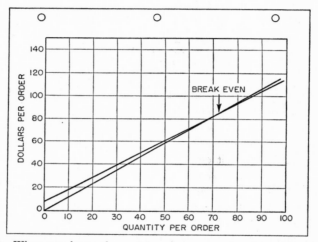

FIG. 50. When you know the cost to process an order through your paper mill, you can find out how much you have to sell to break even on each order.

The figures given by Stanley High apply to purchase orders. Such costs can be quite different from customer order and invoice handling. But such costs are very real. They can have a major effect on your profit figure if you sell low-cost products or spare parts.

We found in one company that it took $85 worth of sales to break even on an order (Fig. 50). Of course, you realize there is no net profit at the break-even point. So our question here is, "How much do we have to sell to make some money?" You can see a rough relation between cost per order and net income in the following table.

REQUIRED DOLLAR AMOUNT OF ORDER

To Make Income, Per Cent	Cost per Order				
	$2	$3	$4	$5	$6
5	40	60	80	100	120
10	20	30	40	50	60
15	13	20	27	33	40
20	10	15	20	25	30
25	8	12	16	20	24

SWAMPED IN PAPER

Next, we sorted sales orders into three groups. The piles were for quantities 1 to 10, 11 to 100, over 100. As a result, we showed that over half our orders gave us only 7 per cent of our volume (Fig. 51).

Per Cent of Orders	Per Cent of Volume
22	77
26	16
52	7

You can easily imagine how much better off the company would be without the 52 per cent of its customer's orders.

I've been through all the arguments. "We can't charge a minimum." Some folks do. Two of my suppliers charge me minimums. Others try to solve this problem with quantity discounts. There are several other methods open to you.

Leo Ault said, "Why don't we fill the order from the customer's letter? And send the stuff to him C.O.D." His method of attack was like the one I proposed in another company. The product itself was costly. Yet, there were numerous orders for spare parts. My comment was, "You have a paper system built to take care of $100,000 orders. I don't know whether you should have two or more procedures. But one method for all orders is wrong. You lose your shirt on the knickknacks."

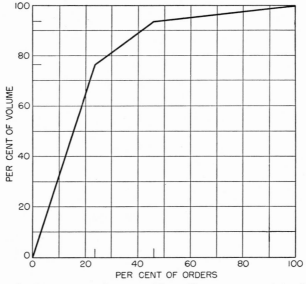

Fɪɢ. 51. Analyze your order quantities. You may expect to find that most of your orders are for a small portion of your volume.

"LINE EXTENSION"

There is another approach. It is related to our earlier break-even per order discussion. However, it is applied in a unique way. Herman Nolen says, "We look upon it as a 'double barrel' method. Double barrelled because it increases volume and cuts costs at the same time. . . . We found . . . that it costs us approximately 18¾ cents to pick, check, pack, invoice and deliver each order line." [2] Then they set about educating customers and salesmen to "extend order lines." They pay "salesmen more for a higher line extension than for a lower line extension." So by increasing the quantity of each item on the order, they solved their problem.

GOOD CUSTOMERS

Dr. Nolen says further, "We also learned that the order line value or line extension was higher when the salesman made the

[2] Nolen, Herman C., *Decreasing Costs by Increasing Unit Sales*, p. 52, *Proceedings*, SAM Conference, November, 1949.

sale than when the order came over the phone or from the want book." That same condition showed up in an order study I made recently. Many orders had the earmarks of having been made out by the stock clerk. Apparently, he kept a pad of purchase orders beside him as he reviewed his inventory cards. As he came to each item that hit its minimum, he wrote out an order. We received as many as a dozen in one day for one item each.

That reminds me of the order filling in a chemical plant. In summer, we had orders to fill that were pages long. These were from colleges that wanted "one bottle of every item on our shelves." Costs mount skyward on such orders. Few concerns are aware of these leaks. When you point them out, the salespeople scream, "But they are our best customers." Sales habits may be supported by management. Both are thinking of dollar volume. Often salesmen are paid commissions on dollar volume. These fellows wouldn't think so much of some dollar volumes if their commissions were based on profitability, as they should be.

SPECIAL SERVICE

Along the same line are special services. Some salesmen concoct "gold-plated trimmings" for standard items in order to make sales. The other way around, they arrange special features the customer asks for and forget to charge more than standard prices.

In this connection, you will be interested in a story told me by John Myers. His telephone rang, and he heard a salesman say, "Do you have any 306's around?" This product was a small item worth perhaps a cent apiece. John said, "I'm not sure, I'll take a look." He spent the next ¾ hour searching and found a substitute. So he called the salesman. The salesman said, "That's fine. I'll telephone the customer in Connecticut to see if these will suit him. You see, he has a credit of 51 cents coming that I want to clear up."

I can see the salesman's side. The fault lies with management for

Not knowing costs and using controls.
Not looking beyond dollar volume.
Not paying commissions on order profits

WHO PAYS FREIGHT?

Another leak is in shipping costs. Some are air-express charges paid because we start too late. Those I want to bring out here affect profits just like cuts in prices.

One concern I worked with couldn't afford to do business outside a 300-mile radius. Their products were heavy and cheap. Yet they shipped to great distances and paid the freight.

Another company shipped some heavy materials from the East to the Far West and South. The freight costs included in prices were based on an average. Averages can throw you way off. Examine a cross section of the facts:

Location	Per Cent Volume	Per Cent Freight	Freight Cost per Sales Dollar
New York..........	33.8	16.3	$.017
Pennsylvania.......	13.0	6.9	.019
Illinois.............	5.8	7.7	.048
Minnesota.........	3.6	6.3	.061
Texas..............	1.8	5.3	.104

In this case, another factor further misled management. The average shipping rate was applied to value. This was another error because manufacturing costs per pound of their expensive products were fifteen times the per pound costs of their cheapest products. Look into shipping costs. They can take away all your profits in some territories. They can wipe out profits on some heavy products.

MAKING UP LOSSES

Whether these things are "sales advantages" or simple losses, you have to offset them. If you lose your profit on $1,000 of sales, you have to sell $2,000 more. One makes up the loss. The other turns in your profit. Said another way, on the $3,000 of sales, you made only one-third of the expected profit. Think of this another way. To make up the loss will take about 12 weeks of productive effort and $2,500 worth of extra facilities.

My impression is that too many of us think in dollars. We seem to rely on mass to overcome odds. Arithmetic doesn't work that way. Some of us may be like the fellow I saw on the subway at Times Square. Everyone had gotten off the train, presumably. It was the last stop. But as the train pulled past me on its way out to the switchback I saw a man soundly sleeping. Maybe, the conductor found him. Perhaps, he made a couple of round trips before he came to.

CHAPTER 17

WHAT PRODUCTS ARE PROFITABLE?

Products are the results of conversion processes. Processes are the causes of costs. Take an example. Suppose you make two styles of an identical product. One is standard. The other is

"Specials" put you in the RED

Special design   Special drawings   Special purchase   Special (delayed) delivery   Special stock

Special tools   Special production   Special bookkeeping   Special costs (higher)   Special profits (lower)

FIG. 52. You lose money on "specials" if you rely upon average costing methods. (*Courtesy of Standard Pressed Steel.*)

"special." Along comes some customer who orders a fur-lined, gold-plated gadget. Does this special go through the same process as the standard? Certainly not. For one detour, it goes through engineering. Then, too, it requires extras in

Order writing	Supervision
Packing	Planning
Billing	Purchasing
Stock control	Timestudy
Machine setups	Accounting

Tom Hallowell portrays these extras better than I can describe them (Fig. 52). They all raise your cost per piece, as I emphasized in chapters prior to this one.

UPSETTING AVERAGES

When you assign such extras to the processes that cause them, their costs will come out of your average overhead. That will change the remainder. If all overhead costs are properly assigned, there is no average overhead to apply. And, you would expect your new costs to differ from the old ones. They will. Some will be greatly different. I remember an instance where,

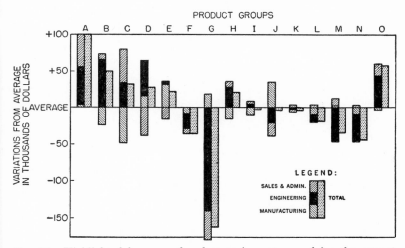

Fig. 53. Highlighted here are the changes in cost caused by the correct charging of engineering expenses.

with corrected overheads, the engineering costs alone of one product were more than the former selling prices of that product.

Marked changes are bound to show up when you shift methods of applying overhead. And if you change also from some other basis to standard time as the measure of productive output, your differences may compensate each other or go largely one way.

The total increase in costs of some products will be offset by the total decrease of others. This is true if the change is due to rearrangement only. But you could get more of one than the other if you also changed volume. This latter effect may be hard to check. You may not know what volume was used in setting your previous burden rates. You may have "just picked numbers out of a hat," scientifically, of course.

In your new process costs, some changes in parts of overhead may offset other changes. Figure 53 shows how engineering-cost changes became a major factor. I like to point this out because engineering cost has been the important one in many plants I have worked with.

SHIFTING PROPORTIONS

Remember, however, that you do not make more or less profit if all you do is rearrange figures. Even so, when you assign overhead costs where they belong, you do much the same thing as shift your product mix. That is important from the standpoint of control. Therefore, here I want to point out our goal by example.

You have often heard someone in your company say, "If it weren't for the gadget sales last month, we'd have lost money." Sometimes the remark is, "Gadget sales are carrying the widget business." That means you have different profit margins. It follows that your profit does change for a given volume, as proportions shift.

To show the effects of shifting, Fig. 54 was drawn. It is oversimplified since it assumes only two types of sales with two rates of profit. If you think of these with caution as two divisions of one line, it will serve its purpose. Many folks do have the case of original and spare-parts sales.

My graph shows diagonal lines representing total volume. If the total income is below the break-even point, of course there is no profit. As the total income goes above the break-even point, profit grows rapidly. So as you move along the top of the graph toward greater volume, you pass to the profit side of the heavy vertical line marking the break-even point.

Selecting one volume like $3,100,000 sales, trace along the diagonal. At the make-up of 90 per cent new–10 per cent spare parts, the profit is about $80,000. With proportions shifted to 70 per cent new–30 per cent spare parts, the profit goes up to about $200,000. At the normal mix, profits are $234,000. If you let your imagination run away with you, and assume all $3,100,-000 to be in spare parts, your profits would be $600,000.

In this chart, we have an extreme range from 2.6 to 19.3 per cent profit for the same income, depending on what we sell. Cer-

tainly such a shift in product mix is not apt to happen. Even so,
I hope I have made the point that all dollars of sales are not
alike. Some add much more to profits or losses than others.

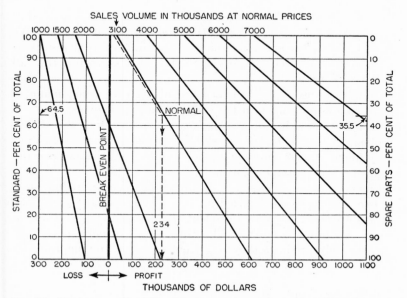

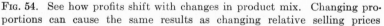

FIG. 54. See how profits shift with changes in product mix. Changing proportions can cause the same results as changing relative selling prices

UPSETTING SALESMEN

With the foregoing picture of shifting product mix in mind, let
us look at profit with your new costs. Some will compare more
or less favorably with your current selling prices. Some will
show profits when you thought you were losing money. These
changes will please everybody. But others will show losses.
Everybody, especially the salesmen, will scream, "Your figures
are wrong." You will have troubles. You will not be heard when
you say, "Listen! What came off of some costs had to go on others.
All I did was rearrange them." They will persist, "But that can't
be right. We always made money on Gadgets." They'll even
bring in your competitor's prices to prove you're wrong.

Everybody will holler about your new costs that go up. They're
afraid the next step is to raise prices. Then they say, "We can't

compete." What they could be thinking is, "We can no longer be order takers."

DOLLAR BIAS

Be careful. Don't fall into the trap of dollar bias. This dollar of sales is not the same as that dollar. It's our fault. We have built quotas and paid commissions and reported results as cents per sales dollar for so long that managers assume that all dollars are alike.

Here's one example. In an Ohio plant, we pushed management to get more work in the shop. The boss kept saying, "We have a $3 million backlog. That's two years' work." We always replied, "All we want are some orders put in the shop." In time, they found that $2.5 million of the "backlog" was engineering design that never would go in the plant.

Here's another. My son Phil came up with some product costs in one plant. He emphasized the losses on a special "line." His pressure caused the Vice-President to react with, "But Smith & Co. is our best customer." This forced Phil to point out, "Yes, and the only products they buy from us are in this unprofitable line."

WHAT IS PRICE?

As a starter, let's look at the factors of price and profit on some product in question. Now, it is wrong to assume that your competitor's price enables him to make a profit. The chances are that his costs are not right. Too, what reason is there to suppose that his price is right? Did he figure his price from yours? Did both of you work from the other fellow's price?

I remember two hot arguments on this subject. Both companies involved are the leaders in their industries. Their question was the same. "How come our smaller competitors have prices 10 per cent lower than ours? Their costs must be lower." I believe two facts are mixed in this viewpoint:

1. These big companies did all the development and design work, and had higher expenses in this part of cost, but

2. The little companies figured their prices as 10 per cent off the leader's prices to get the business. Most people will buy the best name if there is no price advantage.

Then there is the competitor who buys a bankrupt outfit at 25 cents on the dollar. He has lower equipment costs to start with. But he doesn't know how to figure costs. However, he goes after business. Maybe he succeeds. Maybe he follows his predecessor into the sheriff's office.

We can't control profits by following someone else. You must know your own costs. You must determine whether or not to compete at the current prices. Control is what you want.

COURTESY SALES

You can readily see that the type of business you lose money on depends upon how you figure. Obviously, too, when you change the method of figuring, you alter the kinds of business that lose money for you. In several experiences of "taking business apart," I have found that there was always a portion that lost money. Usually, it ran about 20 per cent of the volume. Some was brought to light by the new costing. Some is always with you as loss leader or courtesy business.

When you know you lose money on a product, you don't have to spend money selling or advertising it. There isn't any good reason for wrapping up a 10-dollar bill with each package you ship out. It is a diversionary waste of effort. Besides, you have to make up as much profit on other goods as you lose on the questionable items just to stay even. Therefore, point No. 1 is to control the amount of losing business. In doing this, you start the shift toward a higher rate of profit. Refer again to Fig. 54.

DIFFERENT APPROACH

"What to do," is your next question. Let me start off by saying, "I do not believe in tossing your losing business out the window." First because you have to find something else to fill the space. Second and more constructive, you can't go to work on products you don't have. So it seems foolish to say, "No, thanks. We don't want your orders." Regardless, if you reduce or eliminate some unprofitable business, three things happen:

1. You reduce the total volume of income.
2. You increase the rate of income.
3. You lower the break-even point.

Also, you may actually increase the amount of profit made at the reduced volume. This depends upon the rate of change, of course.

Next in line is to price yourself out of losing business. And surely, you need not spend sales expense trying to get it. But I saw an alternative that worked wonders. Buck & Allen Co. had a number of losing items. One reason was superb finishes with unnecessary tolerances. So the sales engineers went to the customers with a story like this. "Mr. Dodge, we are losing money on this gadget at 21 cents each. We have to get 26 cents for it to make a profit. Now, here is a gadget we can deliver for 21 cents that will do everything required in your motor. And we can make it at a profit to us." Either choice Mr. Dodge made changed loss to profit. It's like the sailor who said to the girl, "Shall we have drinks in your room or mine?"

SKILL FACTORS

Pricing is one side of the profit coin. I don't pretend to know much about that subject. Besides, I prefer Henry Ford's way to make profits—push costs down under prices. From what I've seen done, this is not beyond your organization's capacities. In one plant, I saw several repetitions of such cost reductions. The big Boss sent several notes to the Head of Timestudy that read like, "Get $132 off this cost." In a very short time, the results were there. And all he did was work on the big items. My guess is there was more that could come out.

If your competitor actually does make profits on products that are losing money for you, you should look at your conversion methods. What are his methods of selling, engineering, planning, and producing? In one or all of these major divisions, he may have big advantages over your methods. Here you must decide whether your organization has the aptitudes to utilize such of your competitor's methods as are better than yours. Then you have to determine if the improvements you have to make to catch up will pay for themselves.

USING CONTROL

Dr. Kenneth McFarland said to the 1951 Timestudy and Methods Conference, "Every so often I want to let you know where we are in this speech." Maybe I should do the same here. I started this book with the premise that industry must make profits. I have talked about several factors that affect our knowledge of real profit. The basic fundamental is correct costs. Are they right or wrong? Naturally, our knowledge of profit is wrong to the extent that our costs are in error.

One analytical way to improve cost correctness has been highlighted in preceding chapters. Over-all results were brought together in the profit graph that hinges on the break-even point.

Product mix is another phase of varying profit I have stressed all along. I tried to isolate the effects of material content as a factor in product mix. Then I went to some lengths to show that overhead costs of converting materials to specific products were critical in correct costing and in controlling profits as your product mix shifts.

Correcting overhead costs will uncover new profit and loss facts. As G. Charter Harrison puts it, "The outstanding defect of the conventional profit and loss statement is that it . . . reports profits *made* but it does not show profits *lost.* . . ." [1]

There is no purpose to finding where profits are lost unless you make changes to correct the leaks. You must make changes anyhow, if you continue to progress. The changes to make should be evident, if now your costs are correct. My experiences show, however, that most of us are apt to confuse effect with cause. So from here on, I will try to bring out what to me are the major causes in cost control.

Let me add that change itself is not progress. You may have made mistakes. You must follow up each change to make certain that you get the results you planned. And I firmly believe that you should use incentives to gain and maintain the interests of people in attaining the goals you seek.

[1] Harrison, G. Charter, "The Dead Hand of John Gough," p. 8, Madison, Wis., 1941.

CHAPTER 18

START WITH SALES FORECASTS

Costs are controlled by people. Few of them are mind readers. They need help in the form of better direction finders, better training, and better incentives. These tools have many branches. I don't know enough to write about some of them. Besides, we haven't the space. Just the same, there are several we should touch on. Of these, I want specifically to point up in successive chapters the subjects of

Sales Forecasts   Production Control
Engineering Specifications   Wage Incentives

To my way of thinking, these are the four basic tools you need to make effective use of your cost facts. Let's lead off with sales forecasts because we must have customers' dollars to operate.

OUR LIFE BLOOD

You know as well as I do that industry must have customers. Otherwise, we shut down and there are no costs either to reduce or to control. In the plant, we are apt to overlook the fact that sales come first. I know. I've spent most of my life in the producing end. There we often say, "To hear those guys talk, you'd think this plant was run for the benefit of the Sales Department."

Each of us likes to assume that what he does is important. The salesman has the same right. When this is granted, we get to the basic kick the plant man has. He objects to turning handsprings for the customer he's never seen. He hates to nurse through some special requirement the salesman insists upon. Actually, he prefers to follow a routine. It's easier.

SPECIAL PRODUCTS

Even if he had plenty of warning, the average plant man would prefer not to make the special items. His instincts are right. He knows his costs will be higher. He knows too that the cost figures will not show his added expenses. Why should he welcome any order for "hand-painted" gadgets?

I have insisted that we should get our costs to reflect the facts. That done, we could give production men the proper credit for making the unusual products. Let me add that this type has often shown higher profit margins. I submit that it happens because the customer does the selling. Also, I think that competition is lessened the further you get away from standard products. Despite this, practically every shopman I ever met wants to make thousands of one item.

On this very subject, I had a heated discussion with one president. He had the nicest setup I've seen for making specialties. His company's slogan fitted perfectly. His operations were quite profitable. Yet, he longed for a "standard product."

I concede that salesmen of companies I have known are inclined to "promise the moon" in deliveries and in special trimmings. At one plant, I offered a solution—again of the forced-choice type. I proposed that schedules be set up for additions to price and to delivery schedules for each special feature. These would be added by the salesman to the current prices and delivery promises for standard products. I hoped this would tend to

Reduce the number of estimates for specials.
Raise the prices of nonstandard items.
Lengthen the delivery times for specials or,
Increase the orders for standard products.

All this grows out of my many experiences with "tailor-made" production.

WHY HANG MYSELF?

I cite these problems with job-shop operations first because people say, "You can't forecast sales." But I've been in some plants making high production quantities and they say the same thing. You might conclude that forecasting sales is impossible.

You might argue that way too, if you were the salesman. "Why should I hang myself?" he says. "I'm not a mind reader. How can I tell a year ahead what my customers are going to buy?" He can't, we must admit. Lots of people agree apparently, because I've seen very little forecasting.

AVOIDING SURPRISE

Nevertheless, some folks do plan their sales. In Chap. 11 we worked through a forecast of normal volume. That step has been carried out with little difficulty in several plants. Such a forecast is for one mythical year, I recognize. But isn't any other year's forecast just more or less than the normal year?

Sales forecasting seems to me the foundation for cost control. There are several reasons. First is to avoid being surprised. Costs jump up when you are caught short and try to make good. Production gymnastics are expensive whether you deliver the goods under orders from above or just to show what you can do. The rate of increase is greatest when the time is shortest. And the effect on the shop is most disrupting.

Given half a chance to plan, the shop can avoid a lot of, "Drop everything! Rush this!" It can save setups, scrap, overtime, stock chasing, telephone purchases, and high spot prices. You know all about these excess costs. Then why is it we continue to spring surprises on the shop?

One story may clinch this point. In Bill Maple's shop, they turned out water-conditioning plants for cities. You will admit that predicting sales of once-in-a-lifetime installations is probably the acme in forecasting. In spite of this, Bill had his sales group trained to report "sales likely to conclude in 90 days." He maintained a curve of this forelog of sales. At the bulge of World War II everyone pressed him to get another warehouse. He simply pointed to his forecast. Its curve had turned downward. He didn't need more warehouse space. He might not need what he already had.

SALES PERFORMANCE

Perhaps next in order is the need for measuring what you get for your sales-expense dollars. A survey of selling performance reported by Charles Lapp [1] points out five major weaknesses in sales performance:

"1. Failure to utilize time worked properly.

2. Failure to plan sales effort.

[1] Lapp, Charles, "Supervising Outside Salesmen," Bureau of Business Research, Ohio State University, Columbus, Ohio, 1951.

3. Failure to put in enough selling time.
4. Lack of proper selling methods.
5. Lack of product knowledge."

Concentration on correcting these faults can greatly improve the productivity of the salesman. You should expect to get the same relative productivity from a salesman as from anyone else in your organization. You know the "efficiency" of unmeasured work. Surely, if you know anything about timestudy, you can prove that past production is no index of possible output.

The star salesmen you hear about make "big money." Is that what makes them stars? Are they doing an unusual job, or does it just seem so by comparison? Note, I'm not upset about their take-home pay. More power to them. What I am concerned about here are the gross errors in our measuring stick. We don't know what a salesman should produce. And I'm trying to show that we need more and better forecasts of sales to get the work laid out for them.

On the other hand, intensified selling raises costs and the break-even point. I'm not suggesting that selling costs need go up. I quoted five ways that can be reversed to get higher productivity. Unless you do improve the selling methods, however, you would expect costs to rise with more strenuous sales effort. Remember, salesmen are overhead, and overhead control is our chief concern in this book.

WHAT TO SELL

I think the problem is more basic. You ought to know which way to point before you jump. You should find out what to sell. And "what" is determined by profit. In addition, you need to prepare yourself to direct the salesman's efforts. If you don't, he will sell what the customer wants, or the products easiest to sell, or those paying the highest commissions. In some cases, the more he sells, the more you lose.

Knowing product profitability, you can see where to place the emphasis, either for better methods or for stronger drives. You can concentrate your efforts on the things you do best. You might say that this directing of efforts for an organization is like that for an individual. We think of an individual's aptitudes

and skills. We try to place square pegs in square holes. Why?
To get the best results. Is it not more necessary to plan the operations of a business with the same general approach?

LOOK AHEAD TOO

Important as I'm trying to makes sales for cost control appear
to be, you should think beyond today. What about all the pen-
sions industry is obligated to pay? Where's the money coming
from? What about the millions of unemployment insurance dollars industry must provide if people don't or won't work? Suppose you get the annual wage dumped on top of this heavy load.
Walter Reuther said, "A guaranteed annual wage is the next objective of our union," [2] right after the "Five Years of Industrial
Peace" agreement was reached. The steel settlement in March,
1952, did not include this grant. But the Wage Stabilization
Board suggested "continuing industry-union dickering on the
idea with a view toward reaching agreement on it in a subsequent
contract." [3]

All these add up to necessity for better forecasting. You simply can't afford to be up today and down tomorrow. You have
to shove the peaks into the valleys. Or you should seek other
products to make to fill up your dull seasons. Why not look
ahead and, in the meantime, gain the benefits of sales planning?

SALES COMMISSIONS

To gain better cost control, I believe you need to forecast your
sales and to set incentives to attain your goals. The incentives
to salespeople that I've come across are unsound. As "sales commissions," they are computed as percentages of sales dollars.
Such dollars are loaded with material costs and profit margins.

You may quarrel with my questioning of sales commissions on
material. Others have. They argue that a salesman sells the
whole apparatus. That is one way of looking at it. But the
material content of one product differs greatly from that of another. Some part of your material may be a costly motor or similar purchased unit. I can't stretch my imagination far enough

[2] *New York Herald Tribune,* May 28, 1950.
[3] *Newark Evening News,* Mar. 21, 1952.

to explain how the salesman has anything to do with selling such items that can be purchased where you got them. And at the same price.

Does he sell material? I think it is the conversion he sells. His job is to sell the skill and ability of your organization, not so many dollars worth of metal. I maintain that the material is only the vehicle used to convey the skill and ability of your organization. The material is but scrap metal if the apparatus refuses to function. In reality, then, the customer buys the functioning of your product. He gets the material as the means of transferring that functioning from your plant to his.

Then consider some simple arithmetic. Suppose the salesman's commission is 3 per cent on his sales. Should he maneuver a price reduction of 5 per cent, for example, all he loses is fifteen hundredths of 1 per cent. But the profit has been reduced more than his whole commission. All of the price cut comes out of your profit. You still have to deliver all the material plus all the conversion costs.

No, I suggest that commissions be based on profit and that profit be determined on conversion costs exclusive of material. Even then, I would complicate the formula. My long experience with incentives tells me "to place the incentive in the direction of the goal you want to accomplish." Of course, profit is the chief goal. However, there are others. For example, you want balanced operations. There's little or no profit in rushing with overtime in one department while another is half-loaded. Also, you want to minimize peaks and valleys in the yearly cycle.

SET YOUR COURSE

All this boils down to planning your course of action and directing your incentives to go with it. Any way you look at it, you come up with a forecast of some kind. These forecasts of sales seem to be the most difficult of controls to start. Maybe it's because we try to get the salesmen to make them. Perhaps that is the right way to go at it. But we don't ask the shopmen what they will produce. They are controlled by customer orders.

Should not sales forecasting be approached from the company point of view? Market research and other devices can be used to assist. Several approaches were given in "Forecasting Sales," a report prepared by the Metropolitan Life Insurance Company. Here are three ideas:

"The responsibility for over-all forecasting of sales rests in the budget department which is a staff organization reporting to the president."

"This average forecast is then checked by a forecast committee consisting of the president, the vice president in charge of accounting, the vice president in charge of sales and the economist."

"Most statisticians attempt to compare their company's sales with various published indices in order to determine whether the movements are similar. . . ."

All these look outward from the company, its objectives, and its place in the field. It is more logical to work from market potentials than from past happenstances. And we know that Henry Ford changed the market potentials.

MAKE A START

In the Metropolitan Life report there were many hedges on forecasting such as predicting for a year, for 6 months, and for shorter periods. One method I worked with in 1921 was a 6 months' "running" type (Fig. 55). Each month a new month was added at the end to replace the one just completed. Also, within limits, the sales department could juggle some of the quotas of the months intervening. Basically, the producing departments always had 6 months' work load ahead. They had also 6 months' notice of a rise or fall in the trend.

Having definite goals set is the useful element in forecasts. Presumably, they are based on the needs of the company to meet profit and output quotas. That being so, you are propelled to attain your goals. You try to find out "why" you have any major differences in actual results. You open up many possibilities for improvements that have lain dormant. You begin to control.

This is axiomatic, as I look at forecasting. All the talk about accuracy is hogwash. If sales forecasts are not met, is it the forecast or the salesmanship that is wrong? You have to find out before you can gain control.

Sales forecasting is the generator that supplies the energy to bring in the income and to utilize it to the best advantage. Both

	SEP	OCT	NOV	DEC	JAN	FEB
37511	50	100	50	100	50	50
37512	50	100	100	50	50	50
37513	25	0	50	0	0	25
37514	25	0	0	0	25	0
37515	200	100	150	200	100	150
37516	0	0	0	25	0	0
37517	0	0	10	0	0	10
37518	25	50	25	25	50	50
37519	0	0	0	0	0	0
37520	0	0	0	0	0	0
37521	75	75	50	50	75	50
37522	100	125	100	100	150	125
37523	250	250	250	350	350	200
37524	0	0	0	0	0	0
37525	10	10	0	10	0	0
37526	100	100	200	100	100	200
37527	50	50	25	50	50	75
37528	10	0	10	10	0	10
37529	50	0	0	50	0	0
37530	50	150	150	50	150	150
37531	0	0	0	0	100	0
37532	75	0	0	75	0	0
37533	100	125	150	200	0	0
37534	50	25	25	25	100	125
37535	0	0	75	75	0	0
37536	25	25	25	25	25	25
37537	0	0	0	0	0	0
37538	350	200	100	50	0	0
37539	150	100	150	100	50	25

Fig. 55. Sales forecasts may be made up by months for 6 months on a "running basis" with a new month added each month and some changes made in the earlier forecasts.

revolve about the income available and its equivalent production. You have to know what you can count on before you can risk the changes you know will give you better costs. You must have business to work on to apply the skills of your organization. Trusting to luck is too dangerous.

CHAPTER 19

HOW ABOUT PRODUCTION CONTROL?

"Stop what you are doing and set up this job. The Boss is in a rush for it." [1] That's how Fred Hornbruch portrays the lack of planning. In many shops, we go from one emergency to the next. And, usually, we have a bunch of high-priced supply boys adding to those emergencies. We call them expediters or stock chasers. The more expediters you have, the more evidence you have of lack of planning.

Gene MacNiece says, "Production planning translates sales forecasts into production master schedules. . . ." Later he adds, "Production Control supervises the execution of production schedules so that work flows through manufacturing departments on time and without interruptions." [2]

DELIVERY VS. INVENTORY

Your planning begins with your sales forecast, if you have one. But lots of folks don't. So I'm going to discuss production control independently.

What you want to do is make deliveries on time. You may produce to customers' orders. You may ship off the shelf. Either way, you have need for planning and control. It is simple if you make stock items. It is complex if you turn out engineered products. Always, however, you have to walk a tightwire between carrying too much inventory and disappointing too many customers. Here, inventory is the same whether in process or in stock.

Our problem is to satisfy customers and, at the same time, to have high turnover. To me that means the shortest practical

[1] Bruce, R. T., Jean Chadruc, and F. W. Hornbruch, Jr., "Practical Planning and Scheduling," p. 84, National Foremen's Institute, New York, 1950.
[2] MacNiece, E. H., "Production Forecasting, Planning and Control," p. 5, John Wiley & Sons, Inc., New York, 1951.

process cycle worked backward from the promised delivery date. Let me illustrate with an example.

WAITING AROUND

In Burlington, one day, I was asked this question: "How much stock should we carry? Sales says 3 months. We maintain that 2 months' supply is enough." In reply I stated the basic rule, as I see it. *You need enough in stock to equal the sales you expect in the time it takes to replace your stock.* Then I added, "Your product has roughly six operations with a total standard time of 1.6 minutes. You need stock equal to the sales in that time."

FIG. 56. Much of your process cycle may be lost time spent in waiting between operations.

"You're crazy," said Roy Petty. "It takes 60 days to process one lot." My rebuttal was, "That means your valves sit 59 days 23 hours 58.4 minutes between operations. Is that right?" See Fig. 56.

Then I see the more common problem in the job shop. It reminds me of an incident that occurred on the railroad. I was the youngster. Consequently, I had to run ahead to throw the switch for our gang's handcar. One day, I was a bit slow. Mac, our boss, hollered out, "Hurry up, Phil. There's 50 cents waitin' on a nickel."

I've tried to emphasize this point with Fig. 57. There you see a $6,000 assembly held up. It can't be shipped because packing rings are not ready. This is the kind of thing I've seen in many plants. To overcome the shortage, you may use the method Harold Wells calls "scouring the town in a taxi." What is missing really is production control.

SHORTAGE LISTS

Sometimes a big item holds up shipment. Ironically, it's usually a small part worth very little and easy to get. Why should this be? I suppose it's because all the attention has been given to those parts that take a long time and are unusual.

It's only reasonable to start early with the long-process parts. Many plants get goin' on these as soon as possible. Then they get out "shortage lists." Expediters check off the parts as they push them through. Often, they give shortage lists to foremen or dispatchers. One such list I saw covered 16 pages. It didn't even have "wanted dates" alongside the parts. I couldn't see

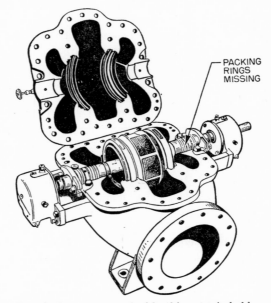

PACKING
RINGS
MISSING

FIG. 57. Much too often a very valuable shipment is held up waiting for a 10-cent item.

how a foreman would know where to begin. All appeared equally important. Chances are that any choices he made would be wrong.

Dates would have helped. They could have supplied priority. I say that because there was no planning to show whether or not the work could be done in any time that might have been set up. Besides, there was no schedule of material procurement to initiate such dates.

WORK LOADS

The work loads kept on IBM cards are little better. The only improvement over dates is the summary of work volume. Again there is no priority and no sequence. One story may suffice:

In a Newark plant, I heard the Drill Press Foreman asking for some work. The Production Manager checked his work load and said, "Bill, you have 4,000 hours of work ahead." "Yes, I know," Bill replied. "All I'm askin' you for is some pieces to drill."

Many of the trick control boards are worthless. They may show volume of work, but there is no sequence. You have no way of knowing whether or not you can get the work out.

I remember my initiation into this problem. John Foster called me in one Friday afternoon to ask if I knew anything about production control. When I said, "No," he asked, "Are you interested?" My reply was, "I sure am." "All right," he said, "I'll see you later." Monday I was put in to replace the nephew of the president. He was gone—no carry-over.

Dave Becker, my predecessor, had a big control board covered with hooks. On these, he hung the old-style price tags with metal rims. The tags carried customers' order numbers and quantities. He lined these up in sequence. He spent nearly every Saturday and Sunday setting up his board. But his tags were all the same size. He lacked volume measures. Hence, by 9 o'clock Monday morning, his board was a wreck. He had six stock chasers in the shop and one clerk in the office. He was at the mercy of the Sales Department. He didn't know what could not be done.

PLANNING PRINCIPLES

John Foster knew what was needed. He told me right quick the two things he wanted:

1. Every order on the books must be on the board.
2. One week's schedule in the foremen's hands at all times.

His first was to guide him on work ahead of the plant. When it slacked off, he went after sales. His second was to give the foremen a week's warning of the jobs ahead. You can see that I was in the middle.

My solution was to set up a long easel. It was about 50 feet long and made of lengths of Celotex. On this, I stuck schedule sheets with thumbtacks. Each sheet was a standard size for one week. It had machines and groups along the vertical edge. Days were across the top, and each day was divided into hours.

On the schedule I drew lines equal to the time lengths of the work to be done. These were drawn in spaces available on machines that could do the work. I had represented by lines both volume and sequence. It was a Gantt chart applied to production planning.

In simple terms, my schedule was like a train of freight cars. I could shift the cars around—change the sequence. But when back together again, the length was still the same—volume of work.

Said another way, if you push in some extra cars, you delay all the others that come after. If somebody pounds the desk, and you move one order ahead of others, the rest are delayed.

SCHEDULE CAPACITY

My freight-train analogy is a bit too simple. In the first place, you can expand capacity by working overtime. In some cases, you can add people. You can break up runs and do other handsprings. But, at a given time, you should define capacity to avoid hiring or layoff. Then your schedule stretches out as work orders increase. This lengthens your delivery promises. When the dates become too distant, you expand capacity.

My freight-train analogy falls short also because usually there are many operations or pieces of equipment. The schedule for each is like a freight train. The cars from one move over into others as the parts progress through their operations.

Look at Fig. 58 to see what I mean. In this example, I have carried 47392 through all the machine tools shown. Each operation time has been blocked in to make this one job stand out. You see illustrated both time-volume of work and sequence of operations.

You say, "That's a lot of detail." It is, but I know of no other way to make a schedule that works. And, a lot of the detailed work doesn't show. For example, when any operation bogged down, we had to reschedule it and, perhaps, all that followed.

All this and the initial scheduling were done from a master card set up for the job. It had on it all operations, and standard times for both setup and operations. These extended by quantity gave the standard time work load. We adjusted this total to conform with the rate of performance. You can see that you must schedule work at the rate it will be "eaten up." Any faster, it will back up. Any slower, you will have waiting time.

	MONDAY			TUESDAY			WEDNESDAY		
MILL	47392	14187	21836		50611	46187	37482		19172
LATHE	18178	47392	35545	20174	18918	50611	46187	37482	
W & S	20174	18178	39109	47392	20174	22046	18918	46187	50611
DRILL	15211	20174	66166	18178	47392	38704	22046		
RADIAL	23319	15211	41441	66403		47392	38704		
GRINDER	52188	23319	15211		18178		47392		

Fig. 58. Gantt type of schedule with 47392 highlighted to show its location in both volume of work and sequence.

FOREMAN'S PART

Almost as soon as I got going, I learned that three more essentials had to be present. The first was that the foreman had to run the work as scheduled. If he couldn't run it for any reason, he had to let me know. That sounds very simple. It is if, as in my case, the boss man wants a schedule that works. He spanked a few foremen who forgot they were part of our organization. Afterward, the schedule worked like a charm.

Second, my schedule had to be right. And here is the crux of the problem. Practical shopmen will ridicule a "new-fangled idea" in any event. But they will continue to do so if it isn't proved right. Therefore, they must not be allowed to thumb their noses at your schedule or you never can find out what's wrong, and fix it.

The third is only a detail. Yet it proved to be a very useful one. It was a rule that the foreman had not completed his work until he delivered to the next department. Making it all one way saved a lot of arguments. It fixed the responsibility as well as kept the product moving.

CHECK PROGRESS

Naturally, there were breakdowns. In this experience there were many. Two factors contributed:

1. We manufactured only to customer orders. Nothing was made for stock.
2. We processed largely with dies and presses, so die failure was a big hazard.

Offsetting these two difficulties was an advantage that seems more important each time I think of it. I had control of the Timestudy-Incentive plan. That work was my primary responsibility. Consequently, we could get all the operations covered and get all the information we needed.

Also as related to scheduling, we knew next morning what happened the day before. Time tickets were turned in every night before the time checkers went home. This permitted the schedule men to check production from part of the time sheets while the comptometer girls worked out incentive premiums on others. Schedule clerks recorded quantities produced on the job master cards. They saw how the production stood. They caught losses, if any. This was important because we had to deliver the quantities ordered.

Then the schedule men drew red lines of results under the blue lines of plans on the master schedule (Fig. 58). Thus we knew where we stood. Revisions were made when necessary. Most rescheduling was done, however, because of emergencies. As I pointed out earlier, the foremen were schooled to run the orders as scheduled. Corollary to this, they notified us by telephone when they couldn't follow the schedule. This enabled schedule to

1. Say what to run in its place.
2. Determine the probable length of interruption.
3. Reschedule all operations affected.

Often rescheduling would move several adjacent jobs. This is evident to you if you think of my freight-train analogy.

Finally, after a 3 months' nightmare, the schedule worked. We added two people to the office and took all six of the stock chasers out of the shop.

DELIVERY PROMISES

Two things cost my predecessor his job. First was his failure to work out a schedule that would stand up. The result was that, second, he was pushed around by the Sales Department. They would quarrel with his delivery promises. Then he'd try to better them. I inherited his headaches.

I'd make delivery promises. Sales would say, "No good. Peerless won't wait that long. You'll have to do better than May 1st." This went on for months. Then when our schedule became sound, the tables were turned.

One day Harry Noble telephoned to say, "Your delivery for Maxwell isn't soon enough." I replied, "I'm only the production control man. You come over and tell me which customer to disappoint." From then on, I put it up to Sales to make the choice. They were responsible, and they knew the customers. I didn't.

Our delivery promises were more reliable. That was our biggest gain. Also, we could make promises almost instantly. We knew there were six bottlenecks in the shop. We checked any inquiry against a miniature schedule of these bottlenecks. If the job had to go through any one of these tight places, we could spot the delivery date quite closely.

COMMON PARTS CONTROL

Shifting to more repetitive operations, I want to relate another experience that ties in with our next chapter. This has to do with parts common to several assemblies. I first learned of it from Bill Beatty of Westinghouse.

Its usefulness depends entirely upon the degree of standardization carried out by engineering. Even so, if you operate only with job orders, you can use all the benefits in part of your work. Too many people follow the all-or-none method. Actually, one system can't be right for all your products. Do not discard all the advantage of stock-order production just because you make specials. Why not plan the production of each part according to its own limitations?

First, find out how many of each common part goes into your finished product. This is a big chore. Then collect all these quantities in one place. This may be done on the stock ledger sheet. A good method is to record the quantities on lists of your finished-product numbers. These lists may be pasted on your ledger sheets. Figure 59 shows this method.

From such master lists, you can establish the total quantities wanted for the period. Let me explain. First, take a look at Fig. 55, Chap. 18. That is the forecast of one product. It is laid out to match the spacing on the list pasted onto the ledger

PART NAME SHAFT					PART NUMBER 52371			
MINIMUM 500		USED ON SW14, AL20			MADE FROM 507			
MAXIMUM 1000		ROUTING C10, B13, A4						
ON ORDER			PROOF	RECEIPTS			ISSUES	
DATE	REQ. NO.	QUANTITY		DATE	ORDER NO.	QUANTITY	QUANTITY	

37511, 37512 (4), 37513 (2), 37514 (8), 37515, 37516, 37517 (1), 37518 (1), 37519 (6), 37520, 37521, 37522 (3), 37523 (4), 37524 (7), 37525 (2), 37526, 37527 (5), 37528, 37529 (2), 37530 (4), 37531 (2), 37532, 37533 (1), 37534 (3), 37535 (10), 37536, 37537 (5), 37538 (5), 37539 (3)

FIG. 59. You can collect common-part usages together on a stock ledger sheet for application against forecast sales quantities.

sheet for part No. 52371 (Fig. 59). When you place the forecast beside the master list, you get your multipliers. Take assembly 37527 for example. The master list shows that five of 52371 are required for one final assembly 37527. The forecast shows:

Assembly	Sept.	Oct.	Nov.	Dec.	Jan.	Feb.	Total
37527	50	50	25	50	50	75	300

For September, you will need 5 × 50, or 250 parts No. 52371. For the 6 months' forecast, you will require 5 × 300, or 1,500 parts total. And so on, for each final assembly quantity given on the forecast.

In addition, you collect all the other requirements for part No. 52371 from any other master lists that may be pasted on its ledger sheet. You simply extend quantities shown on these lists by forecasts for corresponding end products. This is the cleverest device for production control I've ever seen.

MATERIAL CONTROL

Now let me describe a very cute by-product of such a common parts control. Notice on Fig. 59 the caption "Made from 507."

SIZE 1/16"x 1/2"x 120" STRAP COPPER			MATERIAL NO. 507	
PART	SIZE	DECIMAL	QUANTITY PARTS	UNITS MATERIAL
32371	3	.025	48,450	1211
20573	2 1/4	.019	6,740	128
31102	6	.050	750	38
45071	3 1/8	.026	52,170	1357
61033	4 1/2	.038	110,000	4180
			TOTAL	6914

Fig. 60. Put on one list all the parts made from a given type of material. Then you can collect together all your requirements for that material in a forecast production.

This 507 is the number of a standard material size. Suppose it to be 1/16 by 1/2 by 120 inch strap copper.

On a material card No. 507 are all the parts made from this size of material (Fig. 60). Alongside each part number is its size and decimal part of one unit of the standard material.

To this card, you post your production requirements. Then multiply by their decimal equivalents. Add to get your total. Now you have all of one kind of material for your forecast. You can compare these quantities with your raw stores and order the differences.

SHORTS AND SPECIALS

Earlier I said, "One system can't be right for all your products." This applied to short orders and to specials. Repair parts for old designs is another instance. Why should you use the same "system" for these orders that you work out for regular production?

Harry Heywood sent orders of this kind to the toolroom. His toolroom was different from the usual in two respects. One was that all the work done there was on time-measured incentive. The other was that it made some lots of production tools. In so doing, much of the work was subdivided like the shop. There were lathe hands, drill operators, and so on.

Buck Freeman got much the same result by setting up what he called the SOS department. In it, he put units of necessary production machinery. These he manned by highly skilled people. Their work was to turn out all short-run orders.

Buck's idea could be used in many plants. I'm thinking particularly of job shops. There you need men who can remember how the part was made in 1902. The drawings weren't right then and may still not be correct. But the idea has another value. It can be used not only to provide jobs for elderly men whose extra value is in their memories but also to open up another outlet of promotion for those men superskilled in versatility.

Segregation of specials and spare parts seems important to me. For one thing, you get them out of regular production. You reduce the interruptions in your schedule flow. More critical, you do get the parts out. That is very necessary to maintain the good will of your old customers.

PLANNING IS OVERHEAD

Planning is "just more overhead" to many managers. So are accounting, engineering, and timestudy. The value lies in the return you get for your money. I rank it second in degree to timestudy as a cost-control device. Yet most of its value is in the intangible phase of customer relations.

My concern in this book is with its cost-reducing possibilities. This rules out stock chasing. That approach is very expensive, and, as I said before, is the opposite of planning. Real planning cuts the process cycle (Fig. 61). The acme is my exaggeration of the garment people about Toity-Toid Street, New York. They get an order from Macy's, buy bolts of cloth, cut and sew the dresses, and deliver within 10 days to collect the money to pay for the cloth in time to get their cash discount.

Thus planning can greatly increase turnover. You can save lots of space now filled with boxes and pieces of product waiting for processing or a 5-cent washer. You save the damage to product that sits waiting. You save equipment purchased to open up

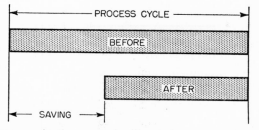

FIG. 61. Better production control will cut down your process cycle and increase your capital turnover.

bottlenecks that would not have existed with good planning. You save setup and teardowns caused by "P.S. change mind," and the extra scrap that goes with extra setups.

Finally, don't overlook the values of good deliveries in getting business. I maintain that when price and quality are equal, you get the business on delivery. Quick promises may get you some orders, but you'd better make good or you're worse off next time. Reliable production control is one of the most constructive tools in cost reduction and control.

CHAPTER 20

DO YOUR ENGINEERS SPECIFY?

"Early in the present century, many fine small companies were engaged in the business of making post holes. They made their post holes carefully by hand, just as each customer ordered them. Each company made hundreds of different kinds of post holes. And each wanted its holes to be as different as possible from the holes made by all the other post hole companies. . . ."

"Many people had to go without the post holes they needed because they couldn't afford them." These quotations are in the start of "The Strange Case of the Seven Sided Post Hole." It is a highly amusing pamphlet published by the American Standards Association. You should read it and give copies to your engineers.

STANDARDIZING

This clever parody points up the values of cutting down the number of your sizes, styles, and designs. If your business is in stylish products, then skip this part. My intention here is to discuss the cost-reducing advantages of standardizing. I will stress the point by quoting from "Simplification in Industry." [1] This is a report made by the British productivity team. It set out to get "detailed practical evidence of the benefits which American producers and consumers had derived from a policy of deliberate reduction in variety in manufactured products, whether materials, intermediate components, or parts, or end products."

Their report cites many examples of drastic reductions. One series shows a range of 29 to 70 per cent reduction of items with losses in sales ranging from .9 to 2.1 per cent. That is like what I found in Salt's Textile some years ago. Ninety-three per cent of the volume was in black velvet. Seven per cent was in 27

[1] Anglo-American Council on Productivity, London, 1951.

colors. Think of the tremendous costs expended in overhead on the "specials."

The report goes on to mention one plant that reduced from 10,000 parts to 3,000. Then with respect to a different company

---

THE DESIGNER

The designer bent across his board,
Wonderful things in his head were stored,
And he said as he rubbed his throbbing bean,
"How can I make this tough to machine?"

"If this part here were only straight
I'm sure the thing would work first rate,
T'would be so easy to turn & bore
It would never make the machinists sore.

"I better put in a right angle there,
Then watch those babies tear their hair.
I'll put the holes that hold the cap
Way down in here where they're hard to tap.

"Now this piece won't work, I'll bet a buck,
For it can't be held in a shoe or chuck.
It can't be drilled or it can't be ground,
In fact the design is exceedingly sound."

He looked again and cried, "At last!—
Success is mine—it can't even be cast!"

Author Unknown

FIG. 62. If you have spent much time in the shop, you may feel as this author does.

it reports, "By 1949 material costs were some 110 per cent above those of ten years earlier, while price to the user had risen by less than 25 per cent. The management expressed the conviction that simplification (standardization) had been a prime factor in keeping down the final selling price." For 140 more such cases, see "Dollar Savings through Standards." [2]

[2] American Standards Association, New York, 1951.

ARTISTIC TEMPERAMENT

I've already stressed the cost finding for "specials." When you know your costs, you can price the "superdupers" so that the choice becomes the customer's. At this point, I want to enlarge upon the kind of cost reduction pointed out by the two cases reported by the British. Many plants can work on this type. They can make marked reductions in the number of styles of similar parts. I see the opportunities when we set timestudy standards for so many parts that differ slightly.

The condition arises, as I see it, for reasons hinted at in the previous chapter. I think we handle our engineering like our production—to order. Each order is treated as an entity. Most people do their timestudy that way. So it is understandable. But why? One reason is lack of cross references. Another is sectionalized design groups. A third is what I call the "artistic temperament." This one is better given by an unknown author in the accompanying poem (Fig. 62).

STANDARDS MANUALS

All kinds of objections are raised to standardizing. The most valid one is the inability to supply spare parts for past produc-

LENGTH \ DIAMETER — CODE	8-32 / 0832	10-32 / 1032	12-24 / 1224	$\frac{1}{4}$-20 / 2520	$\frac{5}{16}$-18 / 3118	$\frac{3}{8}$-16 / 3716
$\frac{1}{4}$ — 2	20832					
$\frac{3}{8}$ — 3		31032				
$\frac{1}{2}$ — 4	40832		41224			
$\frac{5}{8}$ — 5		51032				
$\frac{3}{4}$ — 6		61032		62520		
$\frac{7}{8}$ — 7						73716
1 — 8						

FIG. 63. You can control the number of new designs added to your manufacturing problems by using some form of cross reference that shows the parts you already have.

tion. But if the automobile people used the same argument, many of us couldn't afford to buy cars.

One way to standardize was shown by Ed Brandt. I was present when a new design was brought to him. He picked on a new size of screw. "Why can't you use one we have?" As I remember, the new one was a sixteenth longer. But the engineer didn't add a new screw to the number in stock.

Our control was about like that shown in Fig. 63. The diameters ranged across the top, the lengths down the side. I inserted the codes to show how self-indicating numbers may be set up. In the body of the chart were written the part numbers assigned. Those shown were the stock screws available. Now comes the catch. It took an "Act of Congress" to get a new screw added. Such simple controls held down the number of items. How many different nuts, bolts, and washers do you buy? How much would your costs come down if you were to buy larger quantities of fewer designs?

STARTING CONTROL

Such standardization does save much money when you buy parts outside. When you make them yourself, the savings can be much larger. I used the example of a screw to show what might be done with parts you design and make. Start with the control. Set up ways to cross check any new designs. Limit the assignment of part numbers.

You say, "It's too late now. We have thousands of designs." I can't agree. Two reasons seem valid. First, your company isn't going to stop progressing. That means your engineers are working full speed adding to your line of products. In time, your old designs will drop out. Second, you can make some items of existing designs into interchangeable parts. Each elimination adds to the lot sizes run and reduces setups with incident scrap. Each elimination cuts the costs of

Ordering	Timestudy	And perhaps
Planning	Inventory	Engineering
Costing	Storing	Purchasing

Any combining of part numbers you do tends to increase quantities of like material purchased. This further reduces costs.

But keep in mind the over-all objective. You have to start some-time, or you never do gain the advantages of standardization.

TOLERANCES

Related to "simplification," as the British call it, is another cost-reducing phase that engineering can work on. This has to do with tolerances for interchangeability. "The real way," the budding magnate (Henry Ford) spelled it out, "is to make one like another and as much alike as pins or matches." [3]

We got our start in productivity in 1798 when Eli Whitney introduced the idea of interchangeable-parts manufacture. He laid the foundation for our American standard of living with a contract to produce 10,000 muskets. He developed what all of us now call "jigs."

But jigs, like any other producing equipment, depend upon tolerances. I refer to the variations in the pieces that go into them. The "slop" may go one way or the other. The result is we spend untold millions in "fittin' an' filin' " at assembly. We don't know these losses because they are buried in actual hours or faulty incentive standards. *All such time is indirect labor—rework.* It should be reported separately so you know how much you could spend more profitably in better engineering. In one company, 72 per cent of assembly was rework. In another it was 81 per cent.

To illustrate how bad the condition can be, let me cite one case. I was talking wage-incentive coverage with a company in Connecticut. Their timestudy man kept repeating, "But, Mr. Carroll, we have so many special orders." Finally I caught on. Their special orders were for unfinished parts. Some called for parts completed "through Operation 8," or "through Operation 12." The reason was that the parts in the original machines had been "hand made" at assembly. So the poor guy who needed repair parts had to make them from blanks to fit his machine.

WHY DESTROY INTERCHANGEABILITY

Your problem is twofold. For one, you know what your customer's temperature will be when he gets a spare part that won't

[3] Richards, William C., "Last Billionaire: Henry Ford," p. 76, Charles Scribner's Sons, New York, 1948.

fit. Such reactions can cause you to lose original business. The other is the extra costs created in "making the parts at assembly." That's the part I'm calling to your attention.

Part drawings should be right. They are the specifications the shop should work to. Inspection should check to them. "Limits" are necessary to define acceptable production. Too often, these are either missing or incorrect. Frequently, we find that extremes of pin and hole tolerances will not allow the parts to go together.

I have seen many instances where the foreman insists that work be held to the "high limit." What he is saying is that the tolerance is too wide. On the other hand, I have been confronted with perhaps as many examples of "ridiculous limits."

The American Society of Mechanical Engineers has worked out proper tolerances and allowances. It takes but a few minutes per fit to put these on the drawings. Why not take advantage of what we already know? You can save thousands of hours in costs if yours is the usual shop.

DIMENSIONING

Another pet prejudice of mine is about our methods of dimensioning. We always show dimensions in sections and from both ends. Yet most pieces have to be machined from a locating surface that is at one end.

The shopman must add or subtract to get his working distances. And he does this *every time* the part is made. All the while your expensive machine tool and your inventory are *waiting*. When he makes a mistake, it shows up in the middle. If too long, you may save the pieces. But we don't have any "puttin' on" tools.

The arithmetic is simple, yes. Yet the shopman is much more skilled at his trade. Just the same, I sat on an arbitration case in 1951 where one argument for upgrading a job was for this skill in computing dimensions.

Suppose it does take an engineer longer to dimension the part more practical for shop use. Suppose the engineer gets a higher wage. How many runs do you have to make to break even? How many pieces do you have to save before you make a profit on your investment?

FINISHES

Here's another leak. What finishes do you specify on your drawings? I'll bet no more than the garden variety of *f* mark. All that means is "take a cut on this surface." What kind of a cut? Rough or smooth?

Mark	Type of Finish	Description	Application
rf	Rough finish	Roughing cuts	Flange faces Bottom of bases Shafts for grinding Joints using gaskets
f	Regular finish	Roughing cut and finishing cuts	Ends and tops of cylinders Cylinder and casing bores All pressed fits
sf	Smooth finish	Regular finish with smooth finals	Plungers Shafts and piston rods Shaft sleeves
ff	Fine finish	Polished, lapped, or honed	Thrust-bearing surfaces Valve and seat facings Reversing valves

FIG. 64. Set up modifiers for your *f* marks to tell the shop what the commercial finish is to save unnecessary refinements.

One manager I worked with said, "We saved more money by adopting degrees of finish as you suggested than we did through your incentive plan." Let me add that the incentive installation was very profitable. Perhaps we got drawings improved because the manager was an engineer.

My observations are that the shop does better work than necessary when specifications are not defined. They play safe. They want to avoid criticism and scrap, of course. So we piddle away dollars day after day on unnecessary workmanship.

This may seem to contradict what has gone before. But tolerances and finishes are different. A bearing surface can be as smooth as glass and yet be .015 inch off size and eccentric. Another surface can be quite rough and still be within .002 inch of size and "perfectly straight."

All this adds to substantial savings to be made, probably in your plant, by grading the *f* on your drawings. Determine how many degrees you need. Five or six would be a vast improvement. Then assign some code letters like *r* for rough and *s* for smooth. Put these with your *f* marks to show *rf* or *sf*, as examples. Then, of course, define what you mean by rough, smooth, and your other codes. And go one step farther. Set up examples to show where each type of finish is applied in your products. Figure 64 is a simplified chart that portrays one type of solution.

TOOL DESIGN

Another important cost leak is in tool design. I will touch on this subject here because it is engineering basically. If yours is a hand-made product you will want to skip this section too.

Perhaps the extra costs due to poor tool design result from failure to do the designing in engineering. I'm not convinced. Regardless, the majority of jigs I've seen are not efficient. It takes too long to get pieces in and out. Some jigs have more than one size of nut to tighten and loosen. Others have setscrews that require more time than machining the piece. Generally, the jigs are so far from standardized that you rarely find two alike. All seem to be built to hinder productivity. If you consider two facts, you will see where some important savings can be made by better engineering.

1. Loading and unloading your pieces may take as long as the actual machining.

2. Loading and unloading usually keeps your expensive machines from producing.

I suggest you get detailed timestudies of jig handling. Compare the times for your several designs (Fig. 65). Find what designs are the least expensive for a given function. Then standardize, and instruct engineering to make all new designs to conform. Also, make a study to see what economies there are in modernizing your present jigs.

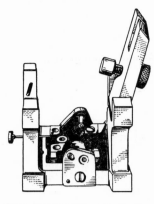

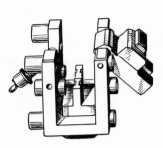

Open construction, easy loading
Standard .050

Extremely confined loading space
Standard .110

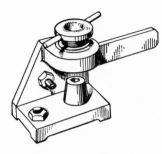

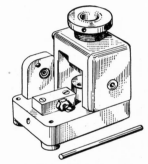

Screw bushing with rod sections
attached

Standard .076

Screw bushing with loose rod
Standard .140

Fig. 65. Study your tool handling to find the designs that will do the job with the minimum of manual time and loss in machine production.

ENGINEERING DELAY

Much that I have said in this chapter calls for more engineering. Taking longer would make matters worse in some plants. The shops already say, "We get the time that's left after engineering dreams over the job for weeks." That seems to be true, in job shops where I have worked.

I don't know, and neither does the shop, how often engineering has to go back to the customer for details. However, more standardization would reduce the time taken up in engineering. Tom

Hallowell omits engineering in the second part of his sketches I stole to contrast specials with standards (Fig. 66). Perhaps too, your engineers could do some of their work in advance. One group that engineers "specials" mostly has tracings printed with

"Standards" keep you in the BLACK

Standard design and purchase Standard tools Standard (fast) production with "standards" from stock Standard (or higher) profits

Fig. 66. Standardizing designs will reduce the costs of overhead operations as well as increase the applications of mass-production methods. (*Courtesy of Standard Pressed Steel.*)

the lines of the standard portions already inked in. I'd guess that roughly half the drawing time has been eliminated.

Whatever you can do to better your engineering "specs" will reduce costs in the shop. Overtime and rushing are expensive. So is extra work of all kinds added because parts won't go together. Keep in mind, too, the costs of having equipment stand idle while mechanics figure out what is wanted. I've often said, "It's cheaper to do the figuring in the office than in the shop."

CHAPTER 21

PEOPLE SPEND YOUR MONEY

Gadgets are what we have talked the most about thus far. Budgets, measures, denominators, and yardsticks are lifeless figures. They are but crutches. They are useful only to the extent and the degree that people use them.

People design the product and inspect it. People sell the product and turn in expense accounts. People write requisitions and buy materials. People purchase equipment and maintain it. People perform operations and scrap material. People supervise work and chase production. People write letters and invoices. Most important, people spend company time in what we call wages and salaries. People spend money. Obviously, then, only people can save money and reduce costs, or spend it judiciously and raise profits.

LOOK OR ACT

Let me emphasize my point negatively. Think of the guy who drives through a red traffic signal. Also recall the two major wrecks on the Long Island Rail Road in 1950 when engineers ran through signals. The red danger signals were not seen or were disregarded. Usually, with both traffic and railroad lights, there are yellow warning signals shown before the red signals. But what difference does color make if people don't look or can't see?

How many times have you seen teen-agers on the street pushing their "wrecks"? Sure, it's all fun and part of growing up. But it's also part of learning that jalopies won't run without gas. There's no difference I can see, whether you try to keep on going when the fuel gauge reads zero, or try to drive a car by a gauge that doesn't work.

We hear this laughingly in the story of the farmer who refused to buy a modern book on agriculture. His reply was, "I ain't farmin' half as good as I know how now." And we see it in the report made by the British productivity team on accounting. "It is true that British accountancy literature contains already the principles of all the techniques in use in the United States, and this Report can do no more than indicate some of the particular applications that have proved effective, *but to take no account of the personal factor in the preparation and use of figures is to overlook the determining factor in the effectiveness* of the accounting branch of American companies." [1]

Cost controls can turn out to be very nicely typed reports. Each head man who gets a copy can say, "Thank you," and places it carefully on his desk. That reminds me of the old-timer. "I'm not afraid of work. I can lie down right beside it and go to sleep."

INCENTIVES FOR ACTION

If you fail to get action, then what? You have two choices, as I see it. You can ask, instruct, order, threaten, discipline, or discharge. That approach is negative—fear of losing the job. I think incentive is better. It is positive. It should be directly related to results. It should be devoid of opinion, or favoritism, or whatever your organization calls "injustice."

People must be interested in working, or the job won't get done no matter what devices we use. You know, for example, that many of our strikes take place in plants where wages are the highest. You may know also that many people working on incentives will not turn out what they can. They restrict production. These facts clearly indicate that money is not the only answer. And they indicate also that something is wrong with the atmosphere. When the attitude is wrong, none of the better methods you introduce will produce the results you expect. People must take action if you are to gain control of expenses. Then, it seems apparent to me that you must provide incentives to make your controls effective. This means everyone who can affect costs should be on incentive. This pertains perhaps more to supervisors and managers than to those who carry on the production. "Chief" Dyer used to say, "If I had to choose between incentives for supervisors and incentives for their people, I would take supervisory incentives." But incentives should be applied throughout your organization.

[1] "Management Accounting, Specialist Accounting Team," p. 37, Anglo-American Council on Productivity, London, 1950.

PAYMENT BY RESULTS

We have many types of incentives. You may think of two, namely, financial and nonfinancial. These are not all. You are thinking of the positive ones. What about the negative incentives of all kinds? Fears for our status, security, pride, and advancement all operate in our day-to-day work. I might add that these, in negative and positive feelings, are all the incentives many firms have. They are the only incentives that exist in large segments of almost every organization.

Incentive is the urge to attain results. It is an attitude or philosophy. Beverly Smith reports a Norwegian engineer as saying, "The strength of America is not in the turn of a lathe but in a turn of mind." [2] That "turn of mind" can be positive or negative. You may see it as a drive "to get some place" or a refusal to "stick out my neck." Naturally, most of us prefer the positive type with rewards for a job well done. The reward can be a pat on the back, a promotion, or increased earnings. The promotion need not carry with it a larger pay check. One incident may surprise you. I sat on an arbitration case that grew out of insistence that a day-turn job carrying a lower base rate was a promotion from night shift.

Coming back to incentives, I frequently point out that there are many incentives more important and more effective than money. But I like money rewards, particularly in connection with cost control. They supply tangible measures of accomplishment. The earnings should vary with degree of control applied. The payments should be closely related in time to the exercise of control.

PROFIT SHARING

It is the remoteness of extra pay from both time and effort that makes profit sharing weak from my point of view. Of course, there are more factual objections. For example, most of an organization can do little or nothing about either the volume or the price factors that greatly alter profit. In the main, all they can work on is cost reduction and control. And do not be confused. The most outstanding example of "profit-sharing"

[2] Smith, Beverly, They Find Us Hard To Believe, *Saturday Evening Post,* Dec. 29, 1951.

success is Lincoln Electric. But is theirs truly profit sharing? Mr. Lincoln describes it as incentive. Actually, the extra money paid to most of the Lincoln people is an added premium proportional to earnings from incentives and suggestions.

Profit sharing is a positive money incentive all right. But the payments, if any, have no direct dependences on standards for costs. Nor do sales commissions and many bonus plans. Yet, such incentive plans can help to reduce and to control costs. The results you get depend so much upon what phases of your plan you talk most about.

BONUS PLANS

Yes, I know that some of the melon-cutting plans give some feeling of participation. So will stock ownership, while the market goes up. That brings up one objection to incentives for cost reduction. You have to pay for results obtained whether the company makes a profit or not. That contradicts the "ability to pay" thesis. "Is that good or bad?" I ask you. Is the ability to pay an incentive or a deterrent? If it were phrased as cost reduction like the General Motors "improvement factor" is stated, it would approach our objectives.

[handwritten margin note: Being Paid To do The Work In The First Place]

All these plans I know about except Lincoln's lack three elements I consider vital. The ability to pay, being out of the control of most of the people, has been mentioned. Then there is the indistinct connection, if any, between constructive efforts made and rewards paid.

The third one is the most damaging. It is the blanketing, leveling, group-system method of paying that disregards individual contribution. For that reason in particular, I favor the use of individual incentive wherever possible.

WORK MEASUREMENT

You need to measure the work that people do and reward extra efforts for basic reasons.

1. People want to get ahead and should be paid for what they do.
2. Costs must be known and predictable if you are to maintain a profitable and progressive company.

Each of these basic reasons has many subdivisions. I will try to point out those that seem important to our subject. Here I want to emphasize, first, that my term people includes all on the payroll. People spend money whether paid on hourly rate or a salary. People spend money whether classified as direct or indirect. People want to get ahead regardless of their positions in the organization.

Second, costs that people can change are the kind we are discussing in this book. They are not only the costs of parts or operations but also those of product overheads. These should be known so that you do not try to steer blindly. These should be predictable so that you don't have to gamble with proposals on new and revised conditions. These must have clearly defined responsibilities for control if you are properly to measure individuals and reward them.

DIRECTED INCENTIVES

Each of us wants to be recognized as an individual. You want to be rewarded according to your own skill and application. And with incentives, you can effect controls that are almost unattainable any other way. With incentives, you can emphasize the objectives you want to attain.

To illustrate, many plants have suggestion plans to reward those who figure out better methods. Some plants pay inspectors an added premium to pick out the defectives. Some companies pay a higher bonus for selling certain products and none at all after quotas are met.

We do the same thing in the shop. We set standards to get more production, but that is not all. We want only so many pieces of a kind, however, so we issue a production order for a stated quantity. With suggestions, we tie these factors together in rewards for savings, not numbers of suggestions. Therefore, incentives are particularly helpful in cost control in that they can be made directional. They can be pointed toward the objectives that you want to attain. These are not necessarily lower costs on the operation involved. As an example, I emphasized in Chap. 20 that increases in engineering cost may be more than offset by cheaper processing. Some plants give the oilcan to a high-priced mechanic because he can prevent costly breakdowns.

Some plants use two mechanics instead of one mechanic and a helper because certain operations can be better balanced with resulting lower unit costs.

EVERY MINUTE

"Every minute starts an hour." [3] That's what six-year-old Paul Gandola said looking at his father's watch. He didn't know the import of his words. You do, however, and their meaning is vital. Time is the largest controllable expense in most companies. Wage cost is said to be 80 to 85 per cent of the total expense in our products. That enormous proportion represents the total from mine to consumer. Your per cent would differ, naturally. It would depend on your section of the total process and what portion of your output was finished goods used in combinations.

Time paid for as salaries and wages is the big element of cost in most plants. The payroll represents people—both direct and indirect. I make no distinction, when it comes to utilizing their time effectively. Right here is where you may find your largest variable in cost. The reason is the lack of control due to the lack of measurement. What work should you get for an hour of time? How much of your payroll time is lost through poor individual performance, faulty management planning, and wasteful extra work? Timestudy will disclose many time facts that help to reduce and to measure costs.

INCENTIVE MANAGEMENT

Again, I say that if incentive is good for some, it is good for all. We need more incentives to bring out the best in people. We should take positive action to offset the trends toward leveling everybody to a common base. Where will our future leaders come from if it isn't worth while to step out of line? Paying more money for the same performance won't do it.

We pound on the theme of better industrial relations at every conference. We repeatedly hear that we neglect the human element in our zest for mechanization. Some of this may be true. However, I do think we must recognize the differences in people that are emphasized in all these admonitions.

[3] Gandola, Paul, *This Week* (*New York Herald Tribune*), June 3, 1951.

Time – Labor is the Controling Factor

James F. Lincoln says, "Incentive Management . . . is a means of giving the opportunity to the individual so that he will develop these abilities of his, now latent." "It is obvious that the Creator in giving to man such abilities expected them to be used." [4] Lecomte du Nouy emphasizes that the desire to attain a superior level is "the trait which links man most clearly to the divine task of evolution." [5] Henry C. Link states, "Personal security comes from habits and beliefs which the individual develops for himself and which make him self-reliant under almost any circumstances." [6]

Paul Hoffman adds, "Our society is organized to promote conditions which challenge the individual to realize his capacities." [7] "Most people never perform at the peak of their abilities," says Daniel Katz. "If they can be motivated to closer approximate their ceilings, then greater productivity will result." [8]

According to Andrew Salter, "No one does what he should. He only does what he can, because that is what he is conditioned to do." [9] In different words, Rudolf Flesch says, "Don't forget that everybody, including yourself, has only his own experience to think with." [10]

OUR HABITS

All these men say in effect, "People have more capabilities than they use." My analysis of that has two facets. One side is given by Myron H. Clark. "It is estimated that less than 20 per cent of the people who are in industry are in that kind of work for which they are best fitted. This means that 80 per

[4] Lincoln, James F., "Incentive Management," pp. 4 and 8, Lincoln Electric Company, Cleveland, Ohio, 1951.

[5] Nouy, Lecomte du, "Human Destiny," p. 244, Longmans, Green & Co., Inc., New York, 1947.

[6] Link, Henry C., "The Way to Security," p. 24, Doubleday & Company, Inc., New York, 1951.

[7] Hoffman, Paul, Basic Elements of a Free, Dynamic Society—Part I, *Harvard Business Review,* November, 1951.

[8] Katz, Daniel, Employee Motivation—Key to Greater Productivity, *The Management Review,* March, 1951.

[9] Salter, Andrew, "Conditioned Reflex Therapy," p. 35, Creative Age Press, Inc., New York, 1949.

[10] Flesch, Rudolf, "Art of Clear Thinking," p. 52, Harper & Bros., New York, 1951.

cent go to their daily work wishing they were in a different vocation." [11]

Add to this what I think is a basic cause. "I got to have more money," is the common phrasing. It starts with the young lad quitting school as soon as the truant officers will allow. He already has a mortgage on a girl and an automobile. So he goes shopping for "bucks." If the man on the east side of the street pays more, he becomes a butcher, a baker, or a candlestick maker. If he can get more on the west side of the street, he winds up as a clerk, a toolmaker, or a locomotive engineer. My guess is that the majority of such choices are purely accidental, prejudiced by the "chance to make more money." From then on, he sells his "experience" at the highest figure. And we keep him in the groove by promotional channels and seniority restrictions. Maybe some day we will overcome part of this by aptitude and psychological testing.

I'm convinced that more square pegs could be put in square jobs by simply rearranging work assignments. This struck me forcibly when I studied 10 girls working on a job in dispute. It appeared to me that five of those I observed should never have been placed on such work. It required a high degree of finger dexterity. However, I'll bet a cigar that interchanging those five with five from across the aisle who had finger dexterity would have eliminated the grievance. Also, I'm sure it would change 10 girls from disinterested attitudes to improved job satisfaction.

Men are moved crosswise in Consolidated Edison's "merry-go-round." The purpose is entirely different. The sideways transfer is to broaden junior-executive development. Yet, I'm sure this left-handed aptitude-interest testing will overcome some initial mistakes. However, generally, more shifts are made upward through promotion. Many are by default. We promote the next in line or the best available.

WHAT NEXT?

Even with better "selection and placement," I think most companies need better measures of performance. My reasoning is

[11] Clark, Myron H., Training Engineers To Handle Men, *Journal of Engineering Education,* Society for the Promotion of Engineering Education, June, 1940.

that two elements are involved beyond getting the right man. First, how will you know if he is the right man without having some gauge of his output? Second, how will you get him to do his best unless you pay him accordingly?

Why should a man serve an apprenticeship to become a tool-maker if he can't earn any more than a drill-press operator working on incentive? How can you get a man to take a promotion to foremanship if he loses money in the deal? How come a Vice-President may decline a much bigger job at a substantial increase in salary that he can keep but a fraction of? These are isolated instances. Their basic causes are distinctly different. Yet, all stem from lack of incentive.

We are going downhill when men decline to do their best. We are losing the advantages of superskills. We are failing to develop the abilities of people when, in effect, we say, "There's nothing in it for you." We contradict our progressive schooling methods when we fix earnings so that the best make very little more than the average.

Obviously, wage incentives cannot solve many of the problems my questions raise. But, they can help. The advantages lie more in stimulating better performances than in the extra earnings paid. Nevertheless, the substantial increases in earnings made possible are important, tangible evidences of accomplishment. We should make the most of both. We need more and better incentives to develop the higher skills in people. I repeat that individual incentives are preferable. They automatically reward those who step out. And goodness knows, we need individual initiative if I correctly interpret the current big to-do about supervisory and executive development.

Winston Churchill says, "We must beware of trying to build a society . . . where enterprise gains no reward. . . ." I agree. I think that we should provide incentives for those who want to work. We should applaud those who prefer working to accepting relief from the State. We should try to lift the poor producer up to the output of the good one—not pull down the good one to the level of the mediocre.

CHAPTER 22

ANALYZE YOUR OPERATIONS IN DETAIL

Your competitors have three basic elements in their costs. These are labor, material, and overhead. Chances are you pay wages and salaries that are about the same. Probably, you pay the same prices for raw materials. You may have the same equipment as they do, or can get it.

What then are the differences? You may say, "labor cost and overhead." That is one way of expressing it. But let's think of these in another form. First, you should recall that a large part of your overhead is wages and salaries. Here I want to put "labor" and overhead "labor" together. U.S. Steel reports these together as employment costs for 1950.

	Per Man Hour
Employment costs..................	$2.12
Products and services bought.......	2.01
Wear and exhaustion...............	.26
Taxes............................	.53
	———
	$4.92

Obviously, most of the item "taxes" comes out of profits instead of costs. Were profit taxes taken out of the 53 cents, the "employment costs" would be a bigger proportion of their total. Probably, yours will be a larger per cent because steelmaking equipment is very expensive. At any rate, people's wages, and the fringe issues that go with them, are the expensive part of cost in most concerns.

METHOD AND PERFORMANCE

How much you spend as "employment cost" depends upon two factors:

1. Methods you use.
2. Performances you get.

217

Methods is a three-sided affair. First is the question of what you do in terms of what you should do. Do you need the super-finish on the back side of your product? Do you have to make 14 copies of your production orders? Do your engineers have to design all parts anew for the nonstandard product? Do your salesmen have to visit your customers every month? Do you have to keep all those records because your President may ask for some information he showed an interest in 10 years ago?

A second side of method is how you do what you think you have to do. Should you turn out that finish on a lathe or a grinder? Should you run off the production-order copies by typing or ditto? Should your engineers make those drawings with pencil or ink? Should your salesmen travel by car or plane? Should you record all that information on Rolldex or McBee cards?

The third side grows out of the second. In many instances of method improvement, you shift costs from wages to charges—for depreciation, taxes, and insurance—the costs of "tooling." Mistakes are often made in these shifts because the costs you used to help decide were not right. They may have been based on actual costs right enough, but the performances that caused those costs are not good. So you should study how effectively people carry out the method you chose.

You know, of course, that you get a much higher productivity under wage incentive than you get with "daywork." You may know also that productivity is higher with individual incentive than under a "group system." Perhaps you are not aware that productivity is higher when incentive is figured daily as compared with weekly.

TIME ANALYSIS

But there is much more to this whole business of how time is spent. A great deal would not be apparent to you unless you were a skilled timestudy man. What the average person fails to see is the waste time and waste effort spent in carrying out whatever methods you have decided upon.

Most people think of timestudy as a method for setting "incentive rates." Actually, it is a means for analyzing work. Much waste can be brought out in the open. Management errors are uncovered. Irregular conditions are observed and measured. Figure 67 illustrates the kinds of time often buried in actual hours. All these bits of time can be evaluated. Parts can be saved. Some work can be eliminated. Each small reduction improves productivity.

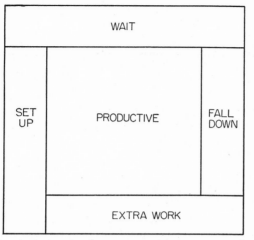

Fɪɢ. 67. Find out what costs of management errors are now buried in your productive labor accounts.

LOST TIME

When timestudy and incentive are used correctly, they point out two types of waste time. One is lost time. The other is wasted effort. Lost time is delay of one kind or another. It is caused by failure to plan or to break down in process. But you lose production whether the delay occurs in the shop, the office, or the field. You can locate and measure the delay by timestudy. The study need not be detailed. You can take steps to remove the causes of delays. Any reductions you secure should improve production and productivity.

Caution. Avoid the mistake of including delays in standards set for incentives. Yes, I know there will always be delays. No plant or office operates without some delays. Just the same, to include delays, you must

1. Pick out some average amount of delay time.

2. Acknowledge that you cannot reduce delays below that amount.

Any average you include is wrong for all circumstances except the average. Delays more than average will adversely affect

incentive earnings. People will complain. You will have difficulties in administering your incentive plan.

The other way, delays less than average will inflate earnings.
The company loses. And I'm not talking about peanuts—the
small change in delays. My concern and yours is with the failure to profit from the progress you make in reducing delays.

Leave delays out of your standards. Give credit for them as
they occur. Then you will know where you stand. Importantly,
you will get a bill for delays with each accounting period. You
will know how much you can afford to spend to reduce them.
By the same means, you will know when you have made progress.
Also, you won't have to revise standards as you correct the
delays.

WASTED EFFORT

Costwise, wasted effort is the same as delays. Scrap is your
obvious example. Rework is another. Yet, we have oodles of
details we do every day that are a pure waste of time. Often,
we carry on whole operations that are wasted effort. These
may be uncovered by timestudy.

Notice, I say "may be uncovered." There are two hedges in
that comment. For one, so much depends upon the skill and
imagination of your observer. He might not recognize the unnecessary work. Then too, in my experience, even more depends
upon the opinion of the supervisor in charge. He has been in
the habit of seeing his work done that way. He is "reactionary,"
as the union calls him. He doesn't want change.

Regardless, all these details add to cost. They are not productive of results. They can be saved. More are to be found
in the indirect operations than in the shop. There are two reasons. First, you have gone over the shop operations many times.
Second, you have a count in the shop. That count is the number
of pieces. With this denominator, you have figured costs. The
cost came down when you made moves in the right direction. In
addition, you worked over the shop operations because of competition or unprofitableness.

GET COST FACTS

You ask here, "Can you put all work on an incentive basis?"
My answer is, "I believe you can." Then I come back with, "Do

you mean on direct incentive based on timestudy?" There are other approaches, as I indicated briefly in Chap. 21.

Most any work can be timestudied. "But is it practical?" you ask. "We can't afford to have one timestudy man for every employee. And what about quality?" One answer to the quality

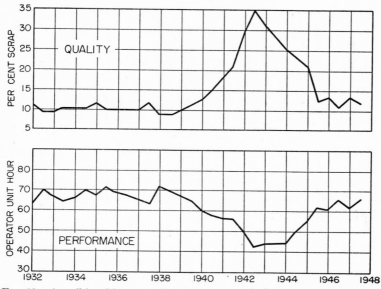

Fig. 68. A striking history of the relation between quality and incentive performances.

question shows in Fig. 68. The whole matter of what is practical depends upon how you look at it.

1. Are you thinking of savings as compared with the costs?

2. Are you concerned about the costs you will have if you don't use incentives?

3. Are you interested in the stability and measure of performance as it affects predicting delivery, cost, and personnel development?

4. Are you considering the work satisfaction that people get from being paid for what they do?

5. Are you aware of the large difference between the work people do and what they could do with better management planning?

6. Are you alert to the cost facts you get from work measurement to replace the unknowns you face without it?

You can ask yourself several other questions. All point to one general fundamental, namely, *timestudy incentive is vastly more important than simply paying people more for producing more.* The cost facts alone contribute more to business success than you have to pay to get them. This is particularly true in the measurement of indirect work.

WORK STANDARDS

When you see the word "incentives," the first thing you think of is work standards for direct labor operations. Most people do. That is as it should be. Standards for productive operations are most important. First, those standards are necessary as the basis for the control of all other costs except direct material. Secondly, as a rule, those standards measure the largest portion of your employment costs. But the same advantages apply to your indirect operations. I want to go into that subject in our next chapter.

But work standards without incentives are like your automobile without gasoline. It won't go far. Sure, you can push it. You can tow it. And that is somewhat like the use of so-called "daywork" standards. You can push people to attain such standards. But remember that, if they don't regularly perform at standard output, your costs will vary.

In contrast, you can attain almost constant costs with a modern one-for-one incentive plan. To emphasize what I mean, let me use a $1.20 base rate for ease of calculation and standard times in Units (minutes).

Output per Hour, Units	Earnings	Cost per Unit
60	$1.20	$.02
75	1.50	.02
90	1.80	.02

My example is only the arithmetic. It becomes a reality when those producing work turn out more than standard quantities. They will, in the usual plant, when the standards are fair. Most employees will turn out 25 per cent more than standard production for a 25 per cent increase in earnings. Two reasons seem to me to explain "why." First is the partial gratification of the inherent urge to get ahead. Second is the basic competitive spirit that pushes all of us to try to beat goals that are set.

VARIATIONS

The condition I have just outlined is ideal. Your plant doesn't operate that way. You have breakdowns, waiting time, extra work, and scrap. You have changes in base rate and salary. You have wide variations caused by volume fluctuations and shifts in the type of output sold. You should have methods and design changes going on all the time. Many such factors continually affect the constancy of labor cost.

But at a given rate like $1.20 per hour, each minute of extra cost is also at $.02 each. Too, when you measure and apply incentives to extra work operations, you reduce their costs. And you need the third basic ingredient, supervisory incentive, to control the nonstandard conditions.

You can see from my simple example that the same constancy exists whether the work done is classed as direct or indirect. You should not overlook this important by-product of incentive. It is very useful in the whole field of cost control. It comes about when you utilize fair work standards with sound incentives based on the modern one-for-one plan. The reasons are

1. Employees earn substantial incentive premiums regularly.

2. Earnings are paid out 100 per cent in proportion to output above fair standard times.

ENSURING METHODS IMPROVEMENTS

Important as constancy of cost is in control, there is another element, more vital, I think. It is the use of work standards and stabilized performances in making more correct predictions. Why I say this is because you cannot afford stagnation. If you are to keep your business alive and healthy, you must make improvements. You must devise new methods, new designs, and new products. These can be hazardous. These involve crystal-ball gazing. Yet, when you have sound time standards and realistic incentive performances, you can predict many outcomes. The ability to predetermine employment cost will remove one large unknown from many of your necessary decisions. Knowing that you will get your money back on methods improvements is so much more businesslike than trusting to luck. You can calculate the savings beforehand when you have sound timestudy data and good incentives. In this way, you can avoid wasting money on opinions. You will not spend money on tools and equipment unless they pay for themselves. That's one side.

On the other side is the value of incentives in gaining employee interest in the success of your new ideas. Elsewhere,[1] I stated that incentive is like a flywheel. A flywheel is a stabilizer, and my experience shows that you get a quite uniform rate of performance with successful incentives. This steady rate of performance is extremely valuable in the predictions we're talking about. The reason is that your people are interested in maintaining their performances and their earnings. This is a vital factor in the success of any new ventures you undertake.

USE STANDARD DATA

To set up work standards, I would take many timestudies of a given type of work. Then, I would summarize these studies in the form of recorded standard data. Recorded data has many advantages. The important ones are greater consistency, more complete coverage, lower cost per standard, and fewer personality clashes. With those advantages, you have a more correct and more complete measurement of production. That is your base line—a necessity if you are to control wage costs.

Consistency in work standards is the important factor in employee acceptance and job satisfaction. These are the foundation of what has been said previously. As I sum it up, "If employees do not make substantial premium earnings, the incentive plan is not a success." [2] Thus, the whole depends upon favorable attitude, and that, I think, stems from fairness.

[1] Carroll, Phil, "How to Chart Timestudy Data," McGraw-Hill Book Company, Inc., New York, 1950.

[2] Carroll, Phil, "Timestudy Fundamentals for Foremen," p. 21, McGraw-Hill Book Company, Inc., New York, 1943.

With data, the standards you set for like operations are consistent. That means your work measurement is fair. Sure, standards can get out of line. They do, if the administration is not carried out forthrightly. But data standards are consistent at the start. And my experience is that your starting consistency can be maintained because revisions are more clear cut and explainable.

PEOPLE MAKE COSTS

In summary, I suggest that you utilize direct incentives to get people to do efficiently what has to be done. And I would set time standards to measure the work that is required and provide the basis for wage incentives.

But I would measure separately all the irregularities. Many can be reduced or eliminated at less cost than it takes to keep them. Here you should use supervisory premium to keep the boss man interested in reducing the variations from standard working conditions. Remember, people spend money. Only people can save money and control costs. Systems won't do it.

CHAPTER 23

WHY NEGLECT THE INDIRECT?

I disagree emphatically with our limited applications of incentives. Why do we overlook the overhead operations? In our shortsightedness, we create earning discriminations. We provide increased earning opportunities for some people and not for others. One result is that some nonincentive folks are given unearned wage *sops*. This destroys incentive. To illustrate, take a $1.00 base rate for easy arithmetic. If you give a 10-cent supplement to a $1.00 an hour base, there remains only a 15-cent differential for the $1.25 incentive earning on a $1.00 base. But incentive is now but 13.6 per cent. That is not enough, in my experience.

Too many of us think only of producing salable pieces. We confine our analysis to supplying our customers. We neglect the indirect work because pieces are not produced by overhead people. But those folks turn out a kind of production. In part, it is like one speaker said during the war, "Believe it or not, we turn out production in Washington. It is waste paper."

INDIRECT PRODUCTIVITY

It's asking too much to expect supervisors to carry all the load. That's why you need measures and incentives for those whom they supervise. Work measures greatly simplify their responsibilities because they state what should be done. Such objective yardsticks wash out many personality problems, gripes, and "slave-driving" attitudes. Incentives reverse the pressures. Both contribute to marked cost reductions.

We don't know how much of our overhead time is wasted. We haven't studied it, as we would have to if it were put on a sound incentive plan. Sure, I know that incentives will not eliminate wasted work. Often, we have incentives and good performances on direct labor operations that we shouldn't do at all. But overhead time is not nearly so well controlled. We can wear out pieces by inspecting them repeatedly. We can repair equipment until it is worth its weight in gold. We can carry our cost systems to four decimal places and produce interminable reports that nobody looks at. Why?

I think these things go on because we have not applied incentives to the work. To move in this direction, we should think first of the microscopes of time and motion study—work analysis. These, in themselves, reduce wasted time but not wasted work. You approach elimination by cost analysis. You ask, "What is the value of this operation in terms of what we spend?" To me, that is the constructive way to improve productivity.

DOES THE WORK FLOW?

Of course, the volume of work turned out may be low because of poor scheduling. To illustrate, let us visualize a conveyer line. As a rule, successive conveyer operations cannot be brought into exact balance. Even if perfect balance in station work loads could be achieved, it wouldn't operate that way. People work at different speeds at different times of the day.

To continue with the conveyer belt, work is delivered at a certain speed. Each successive operation is performed in the time set by the conveyer. Usually, the people adapt their speed to that of the conveyer and take the full time allowed. The same is true of machine-paced jobs. This illustrates the mixture of work and delay.

Occasionally, the productive work is separated from the lost time. In one case, some of the men on a conveyer worked on incentive as rapidly as they could. Then they called for delay time while they waited for the conveyer to catch up to them. In this instance, the extent of the delay time was apparent and supervision could work out methods to utilize it for turning out useful work.

You may think that the conveyer illustration is out of order here. It isn't. I have brought it in on purpose. An imaginary one runs through all sets of successive operations. That bit of theory is important to emphasize the relation of delays to output. With a conveyer in mind, you can more easily see how an hour's delay at one point will show up at each successive operation unless it is overcome somewhere in the sequence. This means higher costs and lower productivity. People pace themselves to the work available. The delays are buried if there is no effect on earnings. On the other hand, you hear about delays when they cut into the new spring suit a person was going to buy with his extra earnings. And delays cost money.

Weekly Salary, 40 Hours	Wage Costs	
	Per Hour	Per Minute
$ 48.00	$1.20	$.02
96.00	2.40	.04
144.00	3.60	.06
192.00	4.80	.08
240.00	6.00	.10

RATIO PLANS ARE WRONG

You may already be thinking, "We should work out some plan for our indirect." If you are, keep away from the oversimplified ratio plans. Paying some percentage of the premium earned by the direct as an incentive to indirect people is basically unfair. There are at least four reasons I want to mention:

1. There is no such thing as a ratio of indirect to direct. Remember your large constant overhead cost?

2. There is no way to adjust the ratio for method changes that occur in both direct and indirect work.

3. There is no controlled way to reduce the wasted time and work buried in over-all indirect costs.

4. There is no measure of individual contribution, skill, or ability.

DON'T OVERSIMPLIFY

Let me illustrate with the setup man. I chose this case because it is the one most often seen. "After all," we say, "he has to set up the jobs or the men can't turn out production." Then we go on to argue, "He's a higher skilled man and yet doesn't take home as much as those he sets up for." Both are true. But those facts do not jibe with the next step. "Therefore, we should base his incentive on the production turned out by those he serves."

First, let me tell you about one instance. I know it is neither typical nor sound. But it does emphasize the error of ratio payment. As commonly done, the setup men were paid the per cent incentive earned by the direct operators. The setup men were expected to turn out the acceptable part for "first-piece inspection."

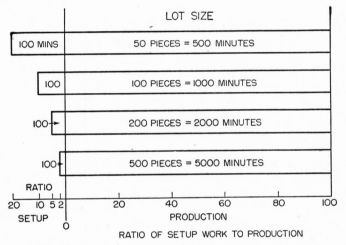

FIG. 69. You can see how markedly the ratio of setup to production falls off as lot size increases.

You're away ahead of me. They turned out a few more pieces. This raised the "efficiency" of the operators and, naturally, the earnings of both. As the practice expanded, more setup men were hired. The added men put more pieces in the operators' tote boxes, and more setup men were needed. And this took place when war-order quantities were rapidly multiplying. More setup men were added when their number should have been greatly reduced. Let's look at it in arithmetic. Suppose the setup time to be 100 minutes and the running time to be 10 minutes per piece. Now study Fig. 69. There I have shown how any ratio of setup declines with expanding production. When the setup of 100 minutes is for a lot of 50 pieces, the ratio is 20 per cent (100 to 500). When the lot size is twice as big, the ratio drops to

10 per cent (100 to 1,000). This alone is reason enough for avoiding the "ratio scheme" of incentive.

Now consider the other type of error. I recall an example. Two truckers supplied material and took away finished products for about 15 assemblers. Under pressure, the Chief Industrial Engineer rigged up a ratio plan. He arranged to pay the truckers the per cent premium earned by the assemblers. When I learned of it, I asked, "What does the plan pay if only one table of assemblers is working?" He replied, "The Unit Hour earned by that table." Then I said, "Suppose only one girl works on production only 1 hour and earns a 90 Unit Hour. What then?"

CAN YOU CHANGE STANDARDS?

Your next question is, "How would you start?" "With time-study," is my invariable answer. Here's the reason. With time-study, you can get four essentials of cost control that are not attainable by any other single method. Let's break the problem down into these four.

The prime factor, to my way of thinking, is a detailed record of the work done. You must have this because operations are always changing. This will be especially apparent if you take any actions to reduce or to control costs. As you change, you must be able to change standards to the new work load.

In my example of the truckers, how would you change the ratio if you introduced a lift truck or a conveyer belt to simplify trucking? How would you compensate them if, on the other hand, you moved part of the assembly to another location or eliminated it? All this put together says: *You must measure the work content of indirect operations so you will know what work is included.* Remember, too, that a ratio would change for any change in either direct or indirect work load.

It follows, also, that unless you measure work you cannot know either how much time is lost or how much work is unnecessary. You find both when you timestudy any task that has been on "daywork." Consequently, you must know that both are buried in any over-all time or dollar amount of indirect. You know that reductions of both through incentive would result in unearned premiums. The end of this chain is "people are earning too much," and your probable remedy is what many call "rate cutting."

Then, the final point is lack of any measure of individual contribution. This is true whenever there are two or more indirect people paid incentive by some such "scheme." The payments are for group work—several setup men and two truckers in my examples. Who did the work? Who has the higher skills?

METHODS ANALYSIS

Second of my four points is the value of work analysis. With detailed study of work done, you can improve methods. You can eliminate much that goes on year after year. Many such operations are those we start but forget to stop. Just to show you what the possibilities are, examine the figures Paul Mulligan sent me that report clerical cost reductions. Those given in the body of the chart are percentages.

Office Dept.	Company						
	1	2	3	4	5	6	7
A...........	59	18	33	41	40	26	37
B...........	20	24	10	41	38	18	19
C...........	31	44	23	23	33	20	29
D...........	54	30	29	...	15	16	19
E...........	21	20	34	...	44	32	22
F...........	31	25	...	...	25		
G...........	43	21	...	...	2		
H...........	21	22	...	...	14		
Ave.......	41	22	26	37	20	25	25

WHAT IS THE COUNT?

The third factor often overlooked in control is the factor of deciding what is to be done. Decision, as I use it here, is in two forms. One is the method selected for doing the work. The other is the decision whether or not to do it at all—by any method—and how often.

My favorite case to show lack of count deals with window washing. In one plant, we set standards and put maintenance men on incentive. The men made very satisfactory premiums.

But—they washed the windows six times in 6 months. Before incentive, I guess it was 6 years since the last washing. This shows how decision to wash or not to wash will change the cost of window washing per unit of salable product.

If you say that any one of your overhead expenses should be 22.0062 per cent of your direct labor cost or of your sales dollar, and it is, you may still be wasting half of it in useless effort. You cannot tell that an operation is either necessary or performed effectively by having your actual cost come out to some set per cent. Where did you get the per cent to start with? From past history or some other plant's yardstick? Neither is more than a numerical gauge of past habits and mistakes.

AT YOUR CONVENIENCE

The problem is much more basic. We do all kinds of things in industry because we have people available to do them. One man told it this way. "Ordinarily, we have five mechanics. In the summer, we have four because one spends full time maintaining Mr. Brown's boat." I'm quite sure there is nothing irregular in this arrangement. My point is that we have four mechanics for 3 months and five for 9 months. And it would be most unusual if the work to be done fell into that pattern.

Yet, this lack of control is very expensive in another direction. The boss calls for some information. We get it for him. Question 1: Was it worth what it cost? Question 2: Did we continue that special report? Question 3: How many other people get copies, with added details, in different arrangement, more frequently that are retyped in other forms with more copies?

Reports are one class of uncontrolled expense. You can think of a dozen more. I classify the whole into three types. I call them necessary, optional, luxury. We have the same kinds of operations in direct labor, but the proportions are different. The reason is that we have had direct operation standards and costs for years. If we decided to do a certain direct labor operation— here is the option or luxury—we have a cost measure of it. Presumably, we weigh this cost against its advantages—real or imaginary. In contrast, we rarely know the cost of the indirect operations. So we cannot compare them with returns for the money spent. How many of these expenditures are economically sound?

COST ANALYSIS

Of course, you can make methods improvements and decisions of "how often" without timestudy. You can eliminate reports, as an example, without knowing time costs. Without timestudy, however, you fail to derive two other sets of facts that are the fourth essential in cost control. You have no breakdown of the constant part of your overhead. We talked about this constant at length in Chap. 8. This setup cost is perhaps the biggest reason why ratios are no good for control purposes.

Then there is the correct analysis of indirect with respect to your several products. This analysis is vital to product cost control. In any period, the products that are relatively more expensive to engineer, to sell, to plan, or to timestudy may be greater or smaller in volume in relation to sales dollars. This was our concern in Chap. 12.

Thus you have four elements besides incentive to reckon with if you really want cost control. You have to know what indirect work is to be done for differing business conditions. You have to set standards "that automatically adjust for changes in the character of the business." You need to know what parts of the large constant indirect costs are reducible by analysis and decision. You ought to make sure what parts of your indirect belong with each of your mixed products. All these facts, important in cost control, can be developed through timestudy analysis. Then, with incentives, you can get people to take selfish interests in controlling costs.

SUPERVISORY INCENTIVES

The work that people do depends a lot on their attitude toward their jobs and their company. Their attitudes are greatly influenced by the type of supervisor you put in charge. That's why he is the key figure in the illustration shown here (Fig. 70). If he has the ability to interest people in their work, the output is higher. If he is progressive enough to look for better methods and interest his group in applying them, the work will move along more rapidly. All this is by way of emphasizing that, in my opinion, the first element in productivity is good supervision.

Supervisors are the people responsible for spending the money. They are the individuals most likely to induce good or poor at-

[handwritten margin notes:]

1. DETAILED RECORD OF WORK DONE

2. WORK ANAL TO IMPROVE METHODS

3. DECIDE WHAT IS TO BE DONE AND WHETHER OR NOT TO DO IT AT ALL.

4. (a) BREAK DOWN OF THE CONST. PART OF OVERHEAD

(b) CORRECT ANALYSIS OF INDIRET WITH RESPECT TO EACH PROD.

titudes. They are on the spots where time and money are spent. They are the people who can most effectively control your losses. Supervisory are the ones most apt to make or to break whatever plan you introduce. To me, these are reasons enough why they

Fig. 70. To make cost control really work, you need three basic elements— (1) work standards to measure productivity, (2) supervisory action to correct lost and wasted time, and (3) real money incentives.

should have incentives to control costs. You should make it very much worth their while to work toward better performance.

Wasted- and lost-time costs are the important factors to consider. Hence, as a rule, you should give payroll cost the most weight in your supervisory incentive plan. Along with this goes the work performances of the people supervised. Putting these together, I suggest 65 per cent for cost control and 35 per cent for employee performance.

Supervisors' earnings should increase as they change lost time to useful production. Their premium should go up further as they help to attain better performances with their people. Both improvements add to productivity.

EXCLUDE BASE MATERIAL

Of course, there are other factors in cost. But do not include in cost control anything that is not wholly within the control of the supervisor. For example, in general, material costs should be considered only in terms of variations from standard amounts. Scrap can be a factor but not the material cost as a whole. Excess tool cost can be included, but not the basic tools themselves. Paper, forms, and other office supplies are properly related only as excesses over some predetermined amounts. Maintenance supplies should affect supervisory incentives only as their amounts differ from established standards.

You can see why these distinctions must be made. The supervisor does not control the basic cost. If you specify engraved bond letterheads, those are the kind to be used in correspondence. If you instruct salesmen to stay at class A hotels, you mean just that—not rooming houses. If you prescribe $\frac{5}{8}$-inch drills, you don't want $\frac{1}{4}$-inch substituted.

Basic costs of materials can weigh heavily in your incentive plan. They may almost completely destroy the sensitivity of your index of controllable variations. The same applies to such items as power, depreciation, and similar expenses, especially those allocated.

WHERE DO WE STAND?

One of the arguments for measuring supervisors was brought out by a group of staff department heads I worked with during World War II. These men were under tremendous pressures to deliver airplane equipment. But they were crying for "some kind of measure" to work against. They couldn't tell how well they were succeeding. As they put it, "All we get to go by are complaints."

They weren't ducking. They "could take it." I know. But they were in the same spot as an executive with a scrap report in pieces or dollars. Without per cent of scrap, he can't tell where he stands. And these important middle management men had

only complaints to go by. They had no way of telling how accomplishments compared with what they should be doing.

SUPERVISORY DEVELOPMENT

There is the other side. Management holds the stewardship
of the business. Managers are people. They give out just like
machines. They must be replaced. With what? With other
managers you develop or steal from someone who did. Assuming you do your share of developing, you need gauges to measure progress—yours in training men, theirs in learning. You
need definitions of the jobs to be done so you can tell what to
train for and whom to measure.

What I'm trying to say applies to all supervisors from gang
leaders up to the top. It begins when you promote a person into
the supervisory channel. It continues as long as promotions are
to be made. You are always faced with upgrading some people to
higher responsibilities. To gauge your progress and theirs, I
maintain you need measures. To spur them on, I believe incentive rewards that vary with individual performances can
stimulate growth as well as indicate achievement.

CHAPTER 24

MORE TOOLS FOR COST REDUCTION

Many spokes go to make up the steering wheel of cost control. I talked about three I consider basic—sales forecasts, engineering specifications, and production control. Then, I discussed work measurement and incentives for both direct and indirect. Dozens of others should be emphasized. But this isn't a handbook. I can highlight only a few more "tools," and then I have to call it quits.

METHODS IMPROVEMENT

Perhaps, the first that comes to your mind is methods improvement. Actually, this one has slipped into several of the preceding chapters. Also, much of those chapters dealt with methods improvements in a sense. They conform more to the broad definition implied in Don Copell's statement, quoted in Chap. 1: "Remember that no war, no strike, no depression can so completely and irrevocably destroy an established business as new and better methods in the hands of an enlightened competitor." [1]

Yet, the "one best way" has not been found. Nor is it likely to be—soon. Hence, there are many things you can improve. Some you can eliminate completely. This is true more in overhead than in direct, as I tried to show in Chap. 23.

Methods improvements are inescapable, if you stay ahead of the parade. You make them by discovering new ways and by copying others. You may have organized methods-improvement activities and trained your people to find better ways. Such efforts can be very profitable. Profits made through cost reductions are every bit as acceptable as profits made on sales, and more lasting. So you should stimulate and encourage your Methods Department. If you don't have one, by all means get

[1] Copell, Don F., "Work Simplification Training," American Management Association Production Series **157**, 1945.

237

a group of imaginative men together and start working without delay.

METHODS CONTROL

Whether you have methods men or not, you must control these costs of changes. You know that many perfectly good ideas and methods are too costly. There is not sufficient quantity for them to pay off.

It may seem silly to you, but you should figure out these things before you spend your money. One reason is that if they won't pay for themselves in one year, probably you should look down the list for better investments. Another is that you can afford only so much per year for improvements. A third reason is that you do not have time enough to follow up on very many innovations to see that you do get profitable returns.

Many of your methods-improvement proposals can be calculated for their economies when timestudy data is available. Yet, I am certain that most are instituted on opinions rather than on facts. People counter with, "That isn't true of our Company. We make a profit every year." Making a profit does not disprove the point at all. Many companies make quite satisfactory profits despite their mistakes. What we want to get at here is the way to improve your average by reducing the number of errors.

In my thinking, a methods improvement should pay for itself in one year. There are two reasons for that time limit. First is the rapidity of obsolescence of ideas in any progressive organization. Second is the fact that special gadgets have only scrap value if the product changes or the company is liquidated. Therefore, the costs of gadgets should be treated as expense.

From this point of view, timestudy data should be used to figure out whether or not an idea is practical. In this, the all-important factor is *quantity*. Sure, the cost of the improvement is often a big item. Also, as a rule, the more costly the improvement, the greater the saving. But the multiplier of quantity is the factor that makes or breaks the change-over. Maybe a diagram will emphasize the point (Fig. 71).

The saving per piece multiplies with the quantity of pieces. The cost to make the change is constant for a given condition. The break-even point is where the total savings equal the cost of the change. If this is at a quantity less than a year's output, then the change is profitable.

Conversely, if there is more cost than savings in one year, it is not a profitable idea from my viewpoint. Here is where some folks begin to argue about the 1-year limit. They want to stretch it to 3 years. To do so is bordering on investment and capitalization.

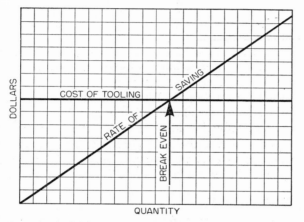

Fig. 71. Quantity is the factor to watch when planning to improve methods.

SEEKING SUGGESTIONS

I try to tell timestudy men that they should pay their way at least three times a year. Some folks say ten times. The point is that we should never be satisfied with existing methods. But timestudy men are only a tiny fraction of the work force. Besides, they have no exclusive rights to making suggestions for improvement. What about the men who make the pieces? What about those who design them? And my biggest gripe is the almost universal rule that says a foreman cannot turn in suggestions. Isn't that silly?

Look at what Lincoln Electric has done with their suggestion plan. They try to get everybody working toward making a better product at a lower cost. Their success is remarkable. One ingredient is the payment of 50 per cent of the net savings for 1 year. Maybe 100 per cent for 6 months would be even better. Making it worth while to turn in suggestions perhaps accounts for the phenomenal rate of productivity growth shown on page 277 of "Incentive Management." [2] Lincoln Electric's average annual productivity increase has averaged 15.35 per cent since 1934. This compares with 3.11 per cent for All Manufacturing and 2.74 per cent for Machinery Industries.

Enlarging awards is only part of the solution. We have to do a great deal more in the way of giving credit and publicity. You know many people will work diligently in their lodge, or church, or union without any remuneration. Actually, they often pay out their own money to aid the "cause."

A third element is necessary too. That is putting the ideas to work. They must be on "display" so that their creators can point to them. Pride comes through the accomplishment.

Why not seek suggestions? Why sit around waiting for them to come in? I think we should stir up, stimulate, ask for, and go after the cost-reduction ideas that lie dormant in our plants. We should advertise, broadcast, publicize, and popularize the cost-reduction ideas that we do get. My belief is that we are daily stepping right over a "gold mine" in our own departments.

WHY SKIP FOREMEN?

The second point I want to pound on is the exclusion of foremen and others from those eligible to make suggestions. Why are they prohibited from adding to the success of the company? I understand the sneaking suspicion that some foreman might steal an idea from one of his men. But why pass up a flock of good ideas because one foreman may be mentally crooked?

If the designers of these plans said, "You can't pay a supervisor by the same formula," I wouldn't object so much. And to make bad matters worse, they say, "It's part of his job." Well, I don't think that inventiveness is part either of his job or of the general characteristics of a good supervisor. Therefore, I think we should devise ways, not profit sharing, to pay any individual who thinks up cost-cutting ideas.

EXCLUDE INTANGIBLES

Some folks shy away from suggestion plans because others have had troubles with their administration. I think one mis-

[2] Lincoln, James F., "Incentive Management," p. 277, Lincoln Electric Company, Cleveland, Ohio, 1951.

FOR SUCCESSFUL SUGGESTION SYSTEM
1. Pay them for it
2. Publicize it
3. Put it to use

take is to open the gates to all suggestions. As a result, many come in that cannot be evaluated. Someone suggests that you paint the shower baths lavender. Another thinks you should have a plant picnic, or a newspaper, or a bulletin board. You cannot compute the worth of such suggestions. So you award $2.

Why not limit the type of suggestions to cost-cutting ideas— those you can figure? Sure, I know the inventor thinks his idea is worth ten times the amount you compute. All of us have the same high regard for our own "brain children." Nevertheless, you can demonstrate the correctness of your arithmetic. Beyond that, it becomes a question of whether or not your formula is acceptable.

MAINTAINING FAIR STANDARDS

I advocate making suggestion plans succeed for another reason. They help to correct the "creeping change" in incentive plans. Incentive should pay for doing better whatever is required. However, method improvements change the work required. Better performances should be rewarded as long as they continue. Better ideas should be paid for once—at the time they are accepted.

I don't pretend for one minute that an excellent suggestion plan will eliminate the creeping change. My guess is that it might solve perhaps only 30 per cent of our problem. That seems to me like a very worthwhile improvement to go after. Besides reducing bickering, you reduce costs. You know that you make no direct savings with improved productivity unless the cost comes down. All this bosh about "saving overhead" just ain't so. To "cut overhead costs by increasing productivity" either you must sell more goods or you must sell the surplus equipment.

PREVENTIVE MAINTENANCE

Another fertile ground for cost reduction is the one we call "preventive maintenance." Let me illustrate with your care of your car. Do you have the oil changed, the battery filled, and the tires checked regularly? Many people do. Still you can't go any place without seeing others at the roadside with break-downs.

Some folks never learn to take care of anything. They seem to think a machine will run forever without care. Maybe they treat their automobiles better than their production machines that turn out their "bread and butter." Anyhow, some people's machines break down with surprising regularity.

Perhaps it's lack of proper training. It may even be lack of discipline. Certainly the man running the machine ought to know that something's wrong before anyone else. If, at that time, he calls attention to the trouble, he may prevent a breakdown.

The same goes for tools and cutters. As they begin dulling, they are easy to sharpen. But the dulling progresses at geometric rates. In no time, you have to grind away large amounts of stock to restore the edge. I know that in tool-sharpening incentive standards, we need several degrees of stock removal. This costs much more money in cutter life than in sharpening time. And all because the machinist ran the tool too long after the edge was gone.

The old saying "a stitch in time saves nine" applies to tools and to equipment. A touch-up can save a tool. A drop of oil can save a bearing. The replacement costs are exorbitant in comparison but often are much lower than the total involved. Think of the overhead not utilized when any part of plant capacity is shut down for equipment repair. Think of the extra costs paid out when you run overtime or buy extra equipment to get out the production lost through shutdown.

I know I just said, "You can't save overhead unless you sell more goods." That is the case after you have bought the extra equipment and the extra plant to house it. Nevertheless, Ben Franklin's idea of a "penny saved is a penny earned" still holds true. Any amount you can raise the "yield" of existing equipment is profitable. It cuts down the necessity for purchasing extra equipment.

USE SPARES

In a related vein, let me bring out an example. I was being shown a cigarette-packing line. Suddenly, the adjuster stopped everything to correct the labeling device. All the machines in the line and six people were made idle. The boss man commented, "The labeler goes bad several times a day." So I asked if they were very expensive. He said, "No." Then my suggestion was, "Why not buy a couple of spares? When one goes bad, replace it with a spare. Then your adjuster can get the defective one repaired while machines and people are turning out production."

Preventive maintenance will help you to "close the stable door before the horse is taken to the butcher shop." Three approaches occur to me. One is to coach people who operate machines in the proper "care and feeding" of their own equipment. Having them call attention to any unusual action or noise is especially important. That may be a symptom of something going wrong. Next is to have regular inspection along with regular oiling.

PATTERNS TO GUIDE

The third I think of is to schedule the overhaul ahead of the breakdown. To do this requires "history" records that few keep. You have to know the pattern of a machine's failure before you can anticipate it. But some folks do know how their machines behave. They can schedule overhauling far enough in advance to have factors of safety.

A story of patterns of employee reactions told here may be doubly helpful. During World War II, Dave Mack said they were having excessive turnover. Analysis of quits showed three high peaks. Let's say they occurred on the fourth day, in the third week, or in the fifth month after hiring. Having learned this, personnel administration could move in ahead of time to make efforts at reselling the company or correcting conditions. Such preventive work greatly reduced their turnover.

QUALITY CONTROL

Along this same line is the basic principle of quality control. In general, the method applies to quantity production. However, the fundamental is based on the probability pattern of a manufacturing process repeating itself. Its sampling is a scheduled checkup based in this case on statistics. And most constructive, to my way of thinking, is finding out the cause of any failure to follow the pattern and getting it back into adjustment. This is "process engineering" as contrasted with inspection.

Your reaction might be that quality control, as I describe it, is not preventive. Yet it is in at least two ways. First is the regular, standardized sampling. The results show when a trend is pointing the way to an "out of control" condition. Second is the corrective removal of cause that prevents continuation of defective production. To the extent that either of these influences the operator to take pride in his workmanship, you gain another very important advantage.

I suggest that the quality-control principle of removing the cause is the best tool of cost reduction we have devised in years. It will produce results. In comparison with "inspection," it is both dynamic and constructive. Much of the inspection I've seen is a pure waste of time. It looks to me as if the parts will be worn out before the customers get them.

These several tools, and many more I could mention, are useful in cost reduction and control. They will make money for you. Remember that a saved dollar this way is just as good as a dollar made on $20 worth of sales—and a lot easier to get in many cases. Also keep in mind that all the productivity increases made by saving time and wasted work raise your yield. With something like a $10,000 cost to provide each job, all these little savings are magnified. I bring this point out again because we are apt to limit our thinking to payroll savings.

CHAPTER 25

CONTROL DEMANDS PROMPT REPORTING

Undoubtedly you have noticed the similarity of management's control function and of quality control. Both take samples periodically. Both try to stay within tolerance limits. Both go into action to remove causes when variances raise costs. But there are important differences.

Quality control establishes limits and works from trend lines. Also, its periodic samples follow percentage scales. In contrast, we see no limits in cost control more definite than "too high." The use of trends is rare enough to be conspicuous. And the periods of sampling are as irregular as the Julian calendar.

USUAL REPORTS

The usual form of operating report has no appeal for me. In fact, I think it is misleading. Comparing "this month" with "year to date" may have some values I cannot understand. It seems to me that, in most businesses, we need a year's total to take in the seasonal change. Hence, January compared with January or February with January plus February gives little or nothing to go by. At the other end, as soon as we get 12 months, we throw away the figures and start over again.

"This month" compared with "same month last year" is somewhat better. But bulk dollar figures uncorrected for volume changes are misleading. If they were shown as costs per unit of standard time, the results could be compared. Even then, some regularity of time interval or percentage sampling is lacking.

A ridiculous incident may illustrate the point. It occurred in a machine shop where our standard called for checking one piece in ten. This inspection requirement was explained to Ed, the operator. But we were chagrined at the end of the day. We discovered him making a mass-production job of his inspection. He was seated at the bench checking every tenth piece that he had put in a separate pail during the day. Unfortunately, most of them were bad. Of course, that meant most of the day's work was junk. Also, he couldn't separate good from bad without inspecting the whole lot.

Whether you check one in ten as you go along or use a statistical sample, you do know where you are all the time. And if you make the adjustments indicated, you still have to watch the gauges in order to hold costs within limits.

CONTROL CURVES

Now I may get my neck out too far. I'll take that risk because I think we need more trend lines to show danger signals. One way to get the results is to use more graphs. I know that many executives shy away from curves and graphs. But how much of that is conditioned reflex? Wouldn't they see trends better if cost results were shown in graph form? I think so. Lawrence Appley points out, "Psychologists tell us that all action is preceded by a mental image." [1]

Don't forget, either, that we have learned a lot about "visual aids" in recent years. Therefore, because you haven't used graphic forms to show results is no reason for not starting now. More and more engineers have moved into management. These men cut their eyeteeth on curves. At any rate, try out different forms. "Keep trying," as I describe it, "until their eyes light up. Then you know you have the right form."

Bill Apple, a very successful manager, has the most unusual set of graphs I ever saw. In his office are what look like ordinary double doors when closed. When open, their two inside faces and the double width space exposed are covered with curves and charts (Fig. 72).

Another manager, Dick Lester, has his figures brought to him in several binders. These stand ready for reference on a sloping lecturn on the table behind his desk. Each binder has a number of curves in it. These curves reflect trends and comparisons between similar control figures. These are kept right up to date. As each new set of figures becomes available, his assistant gets the proper folder, adds the current points, and extends the curves. Then he returns the folder to its place behind the boss.

[1] Appley, Lawrence A., President's Scratchpad, *Management News,* vol 24, No. 2, Feb. 28, 1951.

Maybe the use of curves as controls are habits with them because both men are engineers. I think their methods are good perhaps as a result of the same background. However, I suggest that *rates of change* are what we need to know for control purposes. These you can see most easily in graph form.

Fig. 72. A cabinet of charts points out the trends of changing conditions and the results of cost control.

CURVE FORMS

Curves can be drawn in many ways. They should be, to get the types that reveal the most to the managers. That is a subject by itself. Even so, I'd like to mention two ideas that impress me as useful.

First is that too many curves are drawn on uniform coordinate paper. This form is not too bad, for a single curve. But, usually, there are two or more unlike items on one curve sheet. Examples might be sales, earnings, and man-hours. These three are of different magnitudes. Therefore, fluctuations that are proportional will appear as being out of proportion. Such unlike items should be plotted on semilog paper. Then, like percentage, changes in two or more curves will show as parallel lines. The rates of change will be correctly shown. This is indicated in Fig. 73.

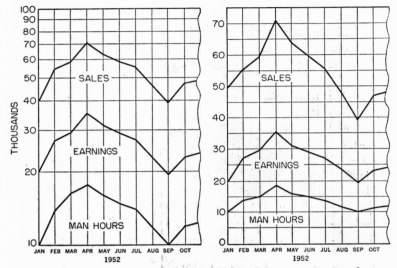

FIG. 73. Comparative trends of unlike magnitudes are more correctly portrayed on semilog scales.

CONDENSED GRAPHS

The second idea has to do with comparisons of current with past experience. The plotting sheet I saw was in uniform cross section. Also, there was one curve per sheet. If used for multiple curves, I would recommend semilog ruling.

The sheet was specially prepared. The right-hand portion was like our regular 20-square cross-section paper with only the heavy lines shown. There were vertical rulings for 12 months. This side is where current performance curves were drawn. The left portion, about a third, had horizontal lines only for plotting previous years.

If one year was shown, then the whole space was used. At the end of the current year, its curve and the previous year's were condensed in the same space. The following year, three years' prior experience could be condensed into this left-hand portion.

And so on. You can get the general idea from Fig. 74. This method is very clever for showing your current and past performances together without having yards of curve paper to monkey with.

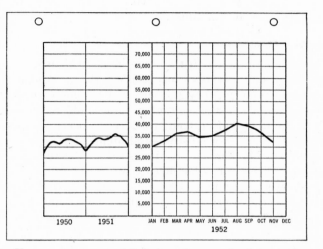

FIG. 74. You may use a special design of curve sheet to condense your past history.

HOW MANY CONTROLS?

Your next question may be, "How many controls should we have?" In reply let me ask a commonplace question. "What controls do you need to operate an automobile properly?" "That's a matter of opinion," you say. And you're right. Yet in New Jersey the men who wrote the law insist upon biannual inspection of brakes, headlights, stop light, horn, windshield wiper, and front-wheel shake. They do not check your speedometer, perhaps because that is difficult. I think it an important control. I'm quite dependent upon my gasoline gauge also. Are you?

Suppose you listed all these and other gauges like temperature and charge. Then, if you asked 10 men to check those they considered necessary what would you get? I'll bet you'd have 10 different sets of check marks. The variety would be much wider if the 10 men were inexperienced with regular auto inspection.

So it is with cost controls. Why do different managers require different controls? Obviously, some have more skill and knowledge than others. Mostly, I think, the differences depend upon background and training—habits if you prefer. But some rely on hunch, "playing by ear," and "common sense." Is that running the business or gambling?

ACCURACY WASTED

There is another side to this question. The mass of detail reported to your supervisors may confuse them. And if the details overwhelm them, they are very apt to ignore them. That reminds me of an instance Stanley Fisher told me about. He was in a discussion of cost control. His supervisors seemed to be lost. So he asked for a listing of all items of $1 or less. When the adding-machine tape of such items was complete, it was about 26 feet long. Here was a horrible example of detail.

Why do we persist in making reports that carry accuracy to pennies? "Centless" accounting is close enough and 10 per cent cheaper, says L. F. Adams.[2] I bring out this point to lead into another more pertinent.

I maintain that accuracy is not important in a dynamic organization. Managers in a company that's going places think in relative terms. They're interested in reports only to see if they attained their goals. They want to know costs only incidentally. Amounts are meaningless because they propose to change them. Successful managers are driven by instincts to improve upon conditions, whatever they are. They are rarely concerned with how much an item actually costs. Rather, they want to know what it *should* cost. Burleigh Gardner says, "Most managements are not interested in a solely 'holding action' in which they seek only to maintain the position of the company. They are builders who want to make things expand and develop." [3]

[2] Adams, L. F., "Centless" Accounting, *The Management Review*, May, 1951.

[3] Gardner, Burleigh B., Working Methods and Personal Effectiveness of Top Managers, p. 3, 9th International Management Congress, Brussels, 1951.

HOW SOON AFTER?

If my premise is correct, then the vital factor is promptness in reporting. If you know that something went wrong yesterday, only one day is lost. If you do not find it out until 45 days afterward, the loss may be 45 times as great. Reporting of change should be as prompt as the radio or newspaper. Then, if you take action as promptly, costs will be in control.

Second, you need the help of everyone who spends time and money. Harold Smiddy puts it this way. "Frequent prompt reports on accomplishments should be rendered. . . . Let the individual man experience a feeling of accomplishment and recognition; possibly reward, thereby securing—that invaluable asset— his enthusiasm!" [4] I would get this by means of incentives. For these to be most effective, the payments must quickly follow the control or lack of it. Daily payments are best. Of course, they are impractical in parts of the organization. I say "daily," however, to emphasize my point of promptness.

Why do you have to wait so long for reports? You don't H. W. Dodge says, "When I first joined Mack, we found that there were 111 reports in the sales department alone. Yet the first thing we did was to initiate a new one—a daily telegraphic report from all over the United States which tells us by noon exactly how many trucks of each model were sold the previous day." [5]

Harry I. Condon says, "Now we are able to produce complete operating statements . . . on the sixth working day after the end of the month." [6] Two companies I know have theirs on the fifth day. Walter H. Dupka gives many suggestions in his paper, "How to Achieve an Early Closing." [7] I think the trouble is in lack of demand. I know management insistence was all it took to get fifth-day operating statements in the two companies referred to here.

[4] Smiddy, Harold F., Managers and Cost Control, *Proceedings,* SAM, p. 5, November, 1949.

[5] Dodge, H. W., *AMA Management News,* Mar. 30, 1951.

[6] Condon, Harry I., Faster Financial Statements, *Systems Magazine,* June, 1950.

[7] Dupka, Walter H., How to Achieve an Early Closing, *The Management Review,* April, 1951

GETTING UNDERSTANDING

Another angle seems important enough to mention. What can managers do with reports if they don't understand them? So I raise this question: "Should the operating people be expected to learn a foreign language? Or should the information be translated for them?" My answer is "some of both."

Your doctor writes your prescription with symbols so you can't translate it. He does so on purpose. Part is "trade secrecy." Part is to protect you from yourself. At any rate, he writes the prescription so you cannot read it.

In contrast, accounting reports are supposed to be for your guidance. They are supposed to be understandable. However, few executives and supervisors have studied accounting. I don't blame them. I haven't either, to speak of. Even so, they must know what the terms mean. They have to learn the lingo.

Currently we are trying to make our "annual reports" understandable to our employees. Some folks are also trying to explain the "American way." This is part of the necessary effort to show employees where jobs come from. We need more of this kind of economic education. We must pound out the same tune over and over again—"Jobs come from customers."

UNDRAPE OUR REPORTS

In the same way we can do much to undrape our accounting reports. Accounting is a *service* function. Its value lies in services rendered. Those services are not paying their way when reports are not read or not understood. One experience that happened to me may underscore my point. Fred White looked at the initial report we brought in and said, "Phil, these are the first figures I have got out of Accounting in 8 years that I can understand." I was relieved and said, "I'm pleased. You see, those have been reduced to eighth-grade arithmetic so I can understand them." He laughed heartily. Thereafter, when I took other reports to him, he would ask, "Are these eighth grade?"

Then he went on to explain. He said, "My trouble with reports I've been getting is that I get lost 'long about the sixth proration when they try to explain what happened."

We need to change reporting to the kinds and styles that mean something to operating people—those who make the costs. And we need to educate supervisors to an understanding of the inescapable fundamentals of accounting they must know.

Elliott Petersen sums up the solution this way: "Records are the instruments of control; they red-light the provoking cost centers for the responsible supervisors. The problem was twofold —make available adequate types of information pertinent to the program, with the least possible delay, and avoid weighty and cumbersome analyses. The solution was a brief weekly report, covering most of the factors, which was to be in the hands of interested parties two or three days after completion of payroll computation." [8]

USEFUL REPORTS

You want prompt reporting that is understandable and brief. Notice, I do not use the term capsule. Here's my reason. A capsule is a cover used to hold medicine such as quinine so you can swallow it without getting the bitter taste. Its use reminds me of the comment, "The subject passed from the notebook of the professor to the notebook of the student without going through the mind of either."

I would not presume to tell you what reports you should have. However, I'd like to suggest several that seem basic to me. First is the daily report of performance of those on incentive. I put that one first because the foundation of cost control is measured productivity. It comes first also because the flywheel effect of consistent incentive earnings is most important to all reliable planning.

Second, you must report all method changes. You have to maintain absolute fairness in your standards of work measurement. They must be correct if they are to continue as your foundation of cost control. If standards are not revised with methods improvement, you inflate your production divisor. You fail to make your cost savings. You run the risk of destroying your incentive plan through the creation of inconsistent earning opportunities.

Third, you should report results to each supervisor. In most instances, these can be weekly. These are the reports I would use as the basis for supervisory incentive payments.

[8] Petersen, Elliott I., Setting Cost Reduction Goals, *Advanced Management*, February, 1950.

In simplest form they consist of three items:

1. Credit for good work produced measured in standard time.
2. Charges for all payroll under his control including his own salary.
3. Costs per standard time unit obtained by dividing charges (2) by credits (1) compared with standards for these costs.

The most critical detail here is credit for good work. In the shop, I'd call this salable pieces. That excludes rework, setup, and extra operations—all indirect labor. In your indirect departments, the same types of exclusions are necessary. Useful output is all you can afford to give credit for. Only by keeping your denominator "pure" can you show rises in cost when costs do go up. Take a simple example. If you retype an invoice and put two invoices in the credit column, you will not see a rise in cost per standard time unit. You paid for two and got only one. So credit only one "good piece produced."

Fourth is to report the relation of indirect to direct. This should follow the same pattern just described except that the divisor (credit) must be your product expressed in standard time This report may divide itself into two. One relates production expenses to product manufactured. The other part relates sales, shipping, and like expenses to product sold.

Costs per standard time unit of output will show you rates. They will reflect changes in expenses, volume, or both. However, remember here the long song and dance I put on about the "constant cost" of indirect in Chap. 8. This will cause changes in costs per unit as volume changes. But you can tell what the cost should be at any volume. For this, you may want to refer again to Volume Variance in Chap. 14.

Fifth is another form of costs per standard time unit. It should be made up to report product costs. Its importance lies in the fact that each product may require different amounts of indirect. Obviously, then, as product mix shifts, you must change indirect expenses. Otherwise, you lose control of costs.

Sixth are the variances you need. I described several in Chap. 14 that seem important to me.

Finally, we come to the accepted standard reports with the Operating Statement that summarizes results. These are indispensable because bankers and stockholders want to know what's goin' on. So does Uncle Sam. However, I put these last because they are results. They are the final scores. Whereas, all my emphasis is directed toward working on the causes. Again I say, "People spend the money." All you can do in reporting is to write down the results.

CHAPTER 26

CONTROL IS TAKING ACTION

Systems can't take action. Neither can figures. Punched holes can't do any more than rearrange figures. People have to take action if you are to get any results from systems or figures.

The action you need should not be limited to once a month—perhaps 45 days afterward—because that is the arrival time of your operating statement. Action should be taken when costs get out of line. And you should know when they are out and how much. More thinking like in quality control would be very productive. Your cost results should be plotted to see if they fall within control limits. And those limits should bear a set percentage relation to your acceptable standard.

FOLLOW UP

To improve the control of costs, your managers should have short informative discussions with their supervisors—weekly if the reports come out that often. These brief meetings should be designed to ask the question "Why?" expecting that the supervisors responsible will find out the causes of any excess costs. Such meetings should develop better execution. They should improve the ability of your supervisors to plan "effect" from a better understanding of "cause."

But remember, the value of these meetings lies in the question "Why?" You must require that reasons be given. You must train your supervisors to realize that cost variations are caused. They don't just happen. They do now, I'll admit. But that is what you are trying to overcome when you undertake to control costs.

Important also is correct timing. You can undermine your efforts by irregular timing. I suggest that your short meetings be held at the same time each week. This detail is essential. The inescapable timing of accounting for results has an unusual psychological effect. Don't overlook it. And here I'm not thinking

of the fear element. After all, you can't get the results you want
if your supervisors are scared to death.

What you are after is control of cost. You want planning for
results—not riding along on the caboose of happenstance. Consequently, you must first make your supervisors cost conscious.
And you know that they will not get that way by themselves.
They can't be bothered. They won't trouble themselves with
things you do not consider important. Hence, you can get real
results from setting up a rigid time of accounting for last week's
performances.

MENTAL AVERAGING

If you really want to get control, you must have standards to
shoot for. Don't stack gains against losses and feel satisfied if
you have a net gain. Don't feel pleased with yourself because
you make an improvement of 20 per cent. The case of a Vice-
President I know may illustrate this point. He planned to employ a consulting firm from Chicago. He told me that two of his
business friends were very favorably impressed with their installations. I asked, "Are they pleased because these consultants
helped them make a 20 per cent improvement?" He said, "Yes.
How did you know?" Then I went on, "What makes you think
it shouldn't have been 50 per cent?" He was a little startled.
His comment was, "I see what you mean."

John Pugsley makes somewhat the same point in a talk before
NACA.[1] He says, "unfavorable variances were not given sufficient prominence when offset by favorable amounts within a
classification of cause, or within a department or works summary." Again, "breaking down the variances separately between
favorable and unfavorable disclosed many recurring unfavorable
amounts. . . ."

You can skim off the cream without much hard work. It
doesn't take very much ingenuity either. But to get better than
average results, you have to take better than average actions.

SIGNING COST TICKETS

Don't think for a minute that you can get any place by having supervisors sign cost tickets. They can do that with their

[1] Pugsley, John, before the 32d Annual International Cost Conference
of the NACA, *The Management Review,* July, 1951.

eyes shut. I'll tell you a story. When I was just starting, they gave me one side of a double desk that belonged to George Bowen, our General Foreman. George came to his desk every morning to sign a stack of time tickets. One day I asked, "Mr. Bowen, do you see what you're signing?" His immediate reply was, "Oh, yes, every one." A few weeks later I was called into Head Office. They had come across a time ticket with George Bowen's signature on it for "Making Paper Dolls."

Signing your name to some ticket is only an indication that the ticket went through your hands. "Follow up" is the important part of getting things done. You must see to it that whatever is decided upon is carried out. More good ideas go to waste because we systematize somewhere along the line. Keep in mind what the Gilbreths wrote. "He never forgot a mistake, either, and so was able to keep making the same errors over and over again." [2]

Ben Graham cites an example that stresses the point the other way around. He is reporting what an accountant told him. "Two years ago I questioned an elaborate tabulated report that I distributed to 37 of our top executives all over the country. All the executives insisted that the report was perfect as it was and that they could not possibly get along without it. . . . The next month I prepared the report, but filed all copies in my desk and not a single question was asked. . . . That was over two years ago and to date I have not had a question about that report." [3]

BEWARE OF REACTIONS

When you start pushing cost controls, you may be surprised at the reactions you get. My experience is that your supervisors will attack whatever standards you set almost as your operators do. My analysis is that it seems easier to them to argue for loosening standards than going to work to meet them.

However, there are two important differences to remember:

1. Too often, managers and supervisors do not have money incentives to meet their standards.

[2] Gilbreth, Frank B., Jr., and Ernestine Gilbreth Carey, "Belles on Their Toes," p. 8, The Thomas Y. Crowell Company, New York, 1950.

[3] Graham, Ben S., Paper Work Simplification, *Proceedings,* 2d Semi-Annual Industrial Management Institute, p. 20, May, 1950.

2. Too often, cost-control standards are based on uncontrolled past performances and, therefore, are already loose.

I readily agree that people may "have more confidence in budgets" they helped to set. But I think it is all wrong to assume that they are competent to judge. Two facts contradict the premise:

1. They have never seen what can be done and thus do not have the benefit of hindsight.
2. They have little knowledge of the whole of business operations and cannot know what proportion their departments' expenses must bear to the total.

Obviously, standards should be right. They should be corrected as soon as errors are discovered. They should be brought up to date as soon as changes are made in work requirements. But the trouble with most of our cost standards is that we have so few facts. We start with what we *did* spend. Such amounts include at least three major unknowns:

1. The degree of efficiency of performance.
2. The per cent protection carried to handle peaks.
3. The amount of unnecessary work done.

In my opinion, you cannot set correct standards by working backward from history. This is particularly true of that great unknown we call indirect—all, and I mean all, the expenses we have above direct labor and direct material. Yet, I hasten to urge that any analytical standards for expenses are better than most managements have now. In the same breath, I want to emphasize that such standards are easy to attain. Also, that substantial improvements should be expected. And that correct standards can be built up only from detailed timestudy analysis of the work that should be done.

NOTHING IS FIXED

You should not assume that any part of your costs is fixed. All can be changed, one way or another. Even the so-called fixed expenses of depreciation, insurance, and taxes can be altered.

One company tore down some buildings after it learned how expensive they were. Two companies I heard about vacated one

plant each, made unnecessary by increases in productivity in
their other plants. And this one amused me. G. D. Crabbs had
asked me to apply incentives to mailing and "sales promotion."
He wanted to get the work out of an old house and squeezed into
the main office. After I reported the job done, he asked, "Is
there anything in our agreement with you folks that will permit
you to touch a match to that old farmhouse?"

HYSTERESIS LOOP

Unless you get action on costs, you will see variances caused by
time lags. When volume increases, your expenses may lag be-

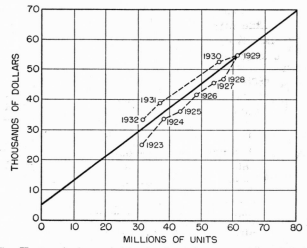

Fig. 75. Hysteresis loop shows the lag of expense control behind the
changes in volume.

hind. When volume decreases, your reductions in expense can
lag even further behind. The path of a complete cycle between
high and low volumes may be a quite wide open loop. Bruce
Wallace originally called this the "hysteresis loop."

Unless your expenses are controlled, their variations lag behind
the changes in volume. As volume increases, the tendency is to
put off giving raises and hiring personnel. You are not pushed
to put on additional employees until the existing force can no
longer handle the volume. We suspect that the increase in business may not last for long. The opposite feeling prevails when

volume declines. An excess in personnel is retained with the hope that business will come back. Expenses are too high during periods of shrinking volume due to

1. Optimism toward the future.
2. Desire to keep the organization together.
3. Failure to detect surplus personnel.
4. Reluctance to lay off excess manpower.

Figure 75 reveals what happened in one concern. You can take this curve as typical of the results of unguided control. Naturally, the periods you analyze must include the two extremes in volume if the loop you get is too close at both ends. However, why not recognize the "facts of life"? You can see that the excess expenses you can have with declining volumes may easily wipe out all your profits.

PEOPLE CONTROL COSTS

Let me repeat that systems do not control costs. You can maintain control only by constructive actions. Again, you have to rely on people to take action. You can help and maintain their interests with incentives. I talked a lot about those in Chaps. 21 to 23. They can, and I think should, be open to all in the organization. As Harold Smiddy puts it, "By far, the large majority of American workmen from 'sweepers to Presidents' budget their own personal affairs so their outlay does not exceed their income. They recognize that as their income goes down, they must cut their expense. Why shouldn't the same rules apply in a large degree to our business enterprises?" [4] He goes on to say, "Top management can lead, and can guide, but the Cost Reduction job to be done is really the sum of hundreds of component items which each of us can best find by applying his own initiative, ingenuity, imagination and integrity to his individual daily tasks." [5]

INCENTIVES TO DEVELOP

Incentives provide the urge to apply those skills we have. Incentives have the double-edged effects of rewarding people for

[4] Smiddy, Harold F., Managers and Cost Control, *Proceedings*, SAM November, 1949.
[5] *Ibid.*

doing better jobs and increasing pay checks without inflation. Also, sound incentives bring out the abilities of your personnel. This is the most valuable by-product in your plans for executive development.

Only people can carry on your organization. So you must develop those who are to take on the load. Malcolm McNair says, "Professional training for business administration is successful only if it produces a goodly number of men with a genius for risk-taking and a capacity for leadership." [6] Part of whatever development plan you have is measuring performances. You can't get results without those gauges.

"Whistling in the dark provides no assurance of survival in a changing world," [7] says Melvin Copeland. You must prepare to keep ahead of changes, and, in the main, your preparations should consist of building your reserve platoon of managerial potentials.

Have you appraised your secondary defense line? Virgil Rowland explains that "appraisal is to determine the present work competence of the individual." [8] He advises you to do it, and I heartily agree. He rates individual potential in eight degrees as follows:

Immediately Promotable	Decision Deferred Because New
Promotable	Questionable
Satisfactory Plus	Unsatisfactory
Satisfactory	Unsatisfactory—Action Date Set

Why wait? Can you develop those you're counting on to take over? How do you know? Can they produce results? What measures have you of their actual attainments?

WHAT INSURANCE HAVE YOU?

Every year we have business failures. This cannot be avoided so long as customers have freedom of choice and business has competition. Those who fail are often those who refuse to change. They insist on staying in a rut. Let's not go by what

[6] McNair, Malcolm P., "The Importance of Being Tough-Minded," Barrington Associates, New York, 1951.

[7] Copeland, Melvin T., "The Executive at Work," p. 120, Harvard University Press, Cambridge, Mass., 1951.

[8] Rowland, Virgil K., Management Inventory and Development, *Personnel*, July, 1951.

the sign on the Alcan Highway reads, "Choose your rut carefully —you will be in it for the next 100 miles." [9] That leads to the one I remember, "The difference between a rut and a grave is the width."

Your customers and your competitors should keep you out of a rut. Added to their pressures, you have another. See what's

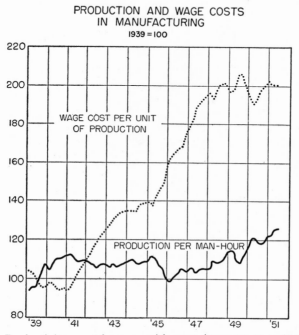

PRODUCTION AND WAGE COSTS IN MANUFACTURING
1939 = 100

Fɪɢ. 76. Productivity must keep up with wage increases or costs will rise. (*Courtesy of Cleveland Trust Company.*)

happening to costs on the average (Fig. 76). Are you staying abreast of this major change? One company carefully watches the relation between productivity—total output divided by total employees—and total wages—base wages, plus fringe benefits divided by number of employees. As long as these two curves are parallel, that company feels it is in good shape costwise. But as soon as the wage-cost curve begins to crowd the productivity curve, everybody gets busy on methods improvements.

[9] Clawson, J. H., Working with Top Management—How Can the Office Executive Best Serve His Boss? *Office Executive,* April, 1951, p. 13.

This cost-control indicator brings together the two factors that show progress. I've often said, "It's not the amount of the wage that counts but what is produced for that wage." Henry Ford proved it when he startled everybody by paying the then unheard of wage of $5 per day. James Lincoln proves it year after year with perhaps the highest average take-home pay in the country.

These are outstanding instances of our general pattern—more goods at lower prices. Most companies strive for the same objectives. Actually, that's what accounts for our American way of life. And I like to think that there is more to be done than we have already accomplished. To make the most of our opportunities, we need to go beyond opinions to get more facts.

What do we get for our money? Facing those facts may be painful. It takes good men who are willing to step out. Show them what has to be done, and pay them for results. Then you will get over the hurdles and take constructive actions that will move us all ahead. Abraham Lincoln said it this way: "If we could first know where we are and whither we are tending, we could better judge what to do and how to do it."

INDEX